Caring for Babies
A Practical Guide

Carolyn Meggitt

Hodder & Stoughton

100348

Dedication

This book is dedicated to Jack Simon Allen, born on the 9 August 1998

Orders: please contact Bookpoint Ltd, 39 Milton Park, Abingdon, Oxon OX14 4TD, UK. Telephone: (44) 01235 400414, Fax: (44) 01235 400454. Lines are open from 9.00–6.00, Monday to Saturday, with a 24-hour message answering service. Email address: orders@bookpoint.co.uk

British Library Cataloguing in Publication Data
A catalogue record for this title is available from The British Library

ISBN 0 340 730765

First published 1999
Impression number   10 9 8 7 6 5 4 3 2 1
Year   2005 2004 2003 2002 2001 2000 1999

Cover illustration by Gill Sampson

Typeset by Wearset, Boldon, Tyne and Wear.
Printed in Great Britain for Hodder & Stoughton Educational, a division of Hodder Headline Plc, 338 Euston Road, London NW1 3BH by Scotprint Ltd, Musselburgh, Scotland.

Contents

Acknowledgements

I gratefully acknowledge contributions from Jessica Stevens, Child care Course Co-ordinator at Southfield School, Kettering. Thanks also to the following people for contributing photos of their babies: Liz Allen for photos of Jack; Mike and Lisa Beevers for photos of Emily; Vicki and Gary Fentiman for photos of Grace; Kate and Paul Fisher for photos of Connie; Lisa Lloyd and Darren Santhorpe for photos of Ashleigh; and Hilary Thomson and Koy for photos of Guy and Doy.

Thanks also to my family, Dave, Jonathan, Leo and Laura, for their patience during my writing hours.

The publisher would like to acknowledge the following photographic agencies: **Lupe Cunha** for pages 36, 58, 168 (top) and 196; **Corbis** for page 121.

Introduction

This book aims to provide the underpinning knowledge for students on child care courses, such as the CCE, the Diploma in Nursery Nursing (CACHE), BTEC child care courses and NVQs in child care.

The book starts from the point that students caring for babies need to feel confident, particularly in the event of an emergency or illness. A special feature of the book is a useful section on first aid and safety procedures, in the Appendix.

Students also build confidence and ability through understanding the rapidly changing needs of babies as they grow and develop. The book provides a thorough review of all aspects of development and includes ideas for stimulating and enjoyable activities to share with babies – fun for baby and carer alike. In order to help students focus on what is fresh in their minds, these suggested activities are grouped together at the end of each chapter.

Throughout the text, students are encouraged to reflect on their practice and to develop expertise in planning stimulating activities and routines for babies. Observational skills are vital in child care, and many of the activities will help to ensure that these skills become a normal and natural part of the carer's daily practice.

While the emphasis of these remarks has primarily been directed towards students of child care, I hope that many of the ideas contained in the book will be equally useful to lecturers and to those already working with babies.

Throughout the book, the baby is referred to as 'she'. This is an arbitrary choice, made to avoid dehumanising the baby by referring to both genders as 'it'.

A comprehensive Glossary may be found at the end of the book, with a Bibliography.

1

Maternal and Foetal Health

Preconceptual care

Life does not begin at birth; the individual is already nine months old when born. In China a person's age is determined not by his birth date, but by the date of his conception. A couple planning to start a family will certainly hope for a healthy baby; preconceptual care means both partners cutting known risks before trying to conceive in order to create the best conditions for an **embryo** to grow and develop into a healthy baby. The first twelve weeks of life in the womb (or **uterus**) are the most crucial as it is the period in which all the essential organs are being formed. The guidelines in Table 1.1 should be considered by a couple at least three months before trying to become pregnant.

Conception and pregnancy

Conception occurs in the **fallopian tube** when the male sperm meets the female egg (the ovum) and fertilises it; the fertilised ovum now contains genetic material from both mother and father – a total of forty-six **chromosomes** and a new life begins.

Early days of life

Within about thirty hours of fertilisation the egg divides into two cells, then four and so on; by five days it has reached the 16-cell stage and has arrived in the uterus (womb). Sometimes a mistake will happen and the ovum implants in the wrong place, such as in the fallopian tube; this is called an

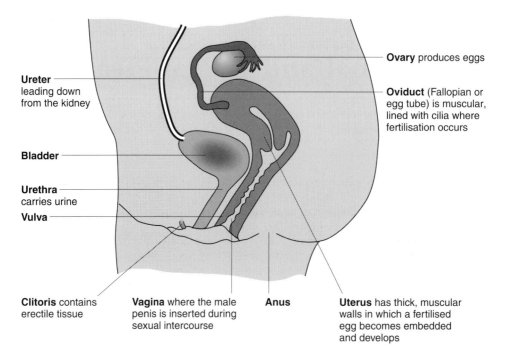

Figure 1.1   The female reproductive organs – a cross-section

ectopic pregnancy. By about the tenth day, the blastocyst has embedded itself entirely in the lining of the uterus and the complex process of development and growth begins. The majority of cells go on to form:

- **the placenta** (called chorionic villi during early development): the placenta (afterbirth) provides the foetus with oxygen and nourishment from the mother via the **umbilical cord** and removes the foetal waste products. The placenta also acts as a barrier to certain micro-organisms, but some may cross this barrier and cause damage to the embryo or foetus.
- **Membranes** or **amniotic sac**: this sac is filled with amniotic fluid and provides a cushion for the foetus as it grows and becomes more mobile.

Fertilisation: only one sperm can fertilise the egg   Two-cell stage   Four-cell stage   Blastocyst

Figure 1.2   Early days of life

Table 1.1 Guidelines for Preconceptual Care

<table>
<tr><td colspan="2" align="center">Guidelines for Preconceptual Care</td></tr>
<tr>
<td>Use barrier methods of contraception
Use a condom or a diaphragm for three months before trying to conceive. It is advisable to discontinue the Pill so that the woman's natural hormonal pattern can be re-established.</td>
<td>Stop smoking
Smoking cuts the amount of oxygen supplied to the baby through the placenta and can result in miscarriage or low birth weight. Some men who smoke are less fertile because they produce less sperm.</td>
</tr>
<tr>
<td colspan="2"> Eat well A balanced diet allows a woman to build up reserves of the nutrients vital to the unborn baby in the first three months:
▶ eat something from the four main food groups every day (potato & cereals, fruit and vegetables, milk & milk products and high protein foods)
▶ cut down on sugary foods and eat fresh foods where possible
▶ avoid prepacked foods and any foods which carry the risk of salmonella or listeria
▶ do not go on a slimming diet; follow your appetite and do not eat more than you need
▶ vegetarian diets which include milk, fish, cheese and eggs provide the vital protein the baby needs;
▶ vegans should eat soya products and nuts and pulses to supply protein and Vitamin B12 may need to be taken as a supplement
▶ folic acid tablets and a diet rich in folic acid taken preconceptually and in pregnancy help the development of the brain and spinal cord</td>
</tr>
<tr>
<td>Genetic counselling
If there is a fairly high risk that a child may carry a genetic fault, such as cystic fibrosis or sickle cell disease, genetic counselling is offered
Tests may be done to try to diagnose any problem prenatally but all carry some element of risk in themselves</td>
<td>Avoid hazards at work
Some chemicals and gases may increase the risk of miscarriage or birth defects. Women should be aware of the risks and take precautions after discussion with the environmental health officer</td>
</tr>
<tr>
<td>Substance misuse and abuse
Do not take any drugs unless prescribed by a doctor. Existing conditions such as epilepsy or diabetes will need to be controlled before and during pregnancy
Many addictive drugs cross the placental barrier and can damage the unborn baby</td>
<td>X-rays
X-rays are best avoided in the first three months of pregnancy although the risks to the foetus are thought to be very small</td>
</tr>
<tr>
<td>Sexually transmitted diseases (STDs)
STDs should be treated – if either partner thinks there is any risk of syphilis, gonorrhoea, genital herpes or HIV infection, then both partners should attend a 'special clinic' for advice and tests. STDs can cause miscarriage, stillbirth or birth defects.</td>
<td>Cut down on alcohol
The best advice is to cut out alcohol completely; moderate drinking (1–2 glasses of wine or beer a day) increases the risk of miscarriage and babies are born smaller and more vulnerable. Heavy drinking, especially in the first few weeks of pregnancy, can cause foetal alcohol syndrome in which the baby is seriously damaged.</td>
</tr>
</table>

The inner cell mass goes on to form the embryo proper.

Until eight weeks after conception the developing baby is called an **embryo**; from eight weeks until birth the developing baby is called a **foetus**. The embryonic cells are divided into three layers:

- **the ectoderm**, which forms the outer layer of the baby, the skin, nails, and hair; it will
- soon fold inwards to form the **nervous system** (brain, spinal cord and nerves) as well;
- **the endoderm**, which forms all the organs inside the baby;
- **the mesoderm**, which develops into the heart, muscles, blood and bones.

At 4–5 weeks, the embryo is the size of a pea (5mm) and yet the rudimentary heart has begun to beat and the arms and legs appear as buds growing out of the sides of the body.

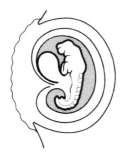

Figure 1.3   Embryo 4–5 weeks

At 6–7 weeks, the embryo is 8mm long and the limb buds are beginning to look like real arms and legs; the heart can be seen beating on an ultrasound scan (Figure 1.4).

Figure 1.4   Embryo 6–7 weeks

At **8–9 weeks** the unborn baby is called a **foetus** and measures about 2 cm. Toes and fingers are starting to form and the major internal organs (brain, lungs, kidneys, liver and intestines) are all developing rapidly (Figure 1.5).

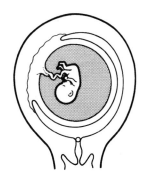

Figure 1.5   Foetus at 8–9 weeks

At **10–14 weeks** the foetus measures about 7 cm and all the organs are complete. By 12 weeks the unborn baby is fully formed and just needs to grow and develop. The top of the uterus (the fundus) can usually be felt above the pelvic bones (Figure 1.6).

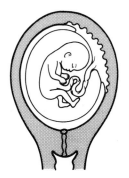

Figure 1.6   Foetus at 10–14 weeks

At **15–22 weeks**, the foetus is large enough for the mother to feel its movements. A mother who has had a child before may have felt fluttering sensations earlier as she is able to identify them. At 22 weeks the greasy, white protective film called **vernix caseosa** has begun to form and the foetus is covered with a fine, downy hair called **lanugo** (Figure 1.7).

Figure 1.7 Foetus at 15–22 weeks

At 23–30 weeks, the foetus is covered in vernix and the lanugo has usually disappeared. From 28 weeks the foetus is said to be **viable** – that is, if born now he has a good chance of surviving, although babies have survived as early as 23 weeks. The mother may be aware of his response to sudden or loud noises and he will be used to the pitch and rhythm of his mother's voice. At 30 weeks the foetus measures 42 cm (Figure 1.8).

Figure 1.8 Foetus at 23–30 weeks

At 31–40 weeks, the foetus begins to fill out and become plumper; the vernix and lanugo disappear and the foetus usually settles into the head-down position ready to be born. If his head moves down into the pelvis it is said to be 'engaged', but this may not happen until the onset of labour (Figure 1.9).

Pregnancy

The signs and symptoms of pregnancy occur after the fertilised ovum has implanted in the lining of the uterus and the pregnancy is usually confirmed

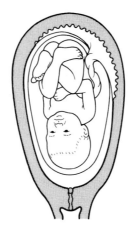

Figure 1.9   Foetus at 31–40 weeks

by a simple urine test – the HCG test, which detects the presence of **Human Chorionic Gonadotrophin** in the urine.

Signs and symptoms of pregnancy

AMENHORROEA (ABSENCE OF MENSTRUAL PERIODS)

Missing a period is a very reliable symptom of pregnancy if the woman has no other reason to experience a change to her menstrual cycle; occasionally periods may be missed because of illness, severe weight loss or emotional upset.

BREAST CHANGES

Sometimes the breasts will tingle and feel heavier or fuller immediately; surface veins become visible and the primary **areola**, the ring around the nipple, will become darker. This is more noticeable on fair-skinned women. As pregnancy continues (at about 16 weeks) **colostrum** can be expressed from the nipple.

PASSING URINE FREQUENTLY

The effect of hormones and the enlarging uterus results in the woman having to pass urine more often than usual.

SICKNESS

Nausea (feeling sick) or vomiting can occur at any time of the day or night, but is usually referred to as 'morning sickness'. Some unlucky women experience nausea throughout pregnancy.

TIREDNESS

This can be noticeable in the first three months of pregnancy but usually lifts as the pregnancy progresses.

The principles of antenatal (or prenatal) care

The main aim of antenatal care is to help the mother successfully deliver a live healthy infant. Women are encouraged to see their family doctor (GP) as soon as they think they may be pregnant. The team of professionals – midwife, doctor, health visitor and obstetrician – will discuss the options of antenatal care, type of delivery and post-natal care with the mother. Antenatal care has the following principles or aims:

- a safe pregnancy and delivery resulting in a healthy mother and baby;
- the identification and management of any deviation from normal;
- preparation of both parents for labour and parenthood;
- to provide an emotionally satisfying experience;
- promotion of a healthy lifestyle and breastfeeding.

The management of antenatal care

Statutory services relating to antenatal care

The first decision to be made is **where** the birth will take place. Facilities and policies vary a great deal around the UK and some people have more choices than others do. The options are:

▶ **Home** – some doctors do not agree with home births in any circumstances as they are concerned about the lack of hospital facilities if anything should go wrong during labour; the woman is entitled to register with another doctor if she wishes to have a home birth. Antenatal care is shared between the community midwife, who visits the woman in her own home or at a health centre, and the GP.

▶ **Hospital** – a full stay in hospital is usually 7 or 8 days, but there are often options to stay only 48 hours or even 6 hours. Antenatal care is shared between the hospital, the GP and the community midwife.

▶ **GP Units** – These are run by GPs and community midwives, often using beds within a district hospital or in a separate building near the hospital.

▶ **Midwife Unit** – This unit is run entirely by midwives who undertake all the antenatal care, delivery and postnatal care. The mother and baby usually stay in the unit from six hours after birth to three days. Midwife units are not widely available.

▶ **Domino schemes** – Domino is an abbreviation of Domiciliary-in-out. Care is shared between the community midwife and the GP. When labour starts, the midwife comes into the hospital or GP unit to deliver the baby. Back up care can be from the woman's GP or from a hospital doctor. If both mother and baby are well, they can often go home within hours of the birth and the midwife continues to look after them at home.

Professionals involved in antenatal care and childbirth

MIDWIFE

This is a registered nurse who has had further training in the care of women during pregnancy and labour. They can work in hospitals, clinics or in the community. Most routine antenatal care is carried out by midwives and a midwife delivers most babies born in the UK. In the community midwives have a statutory responsibility to care for both mother and baby for 10 days after delivery.

GENERAL PRACTITIONER (GP) OR FAMILY DOCTOR

This is a doctor who has taken further training in general practice. Many GP group practices also have a doctor who has taken further training in obstetrics.

OBSTETRICIAN

This is a doctor who has specialised in the care of pregnant women and childbirth. Most of their work is carried out in hospital maternity units and they care for women who have complications in pregnancy or who need a Caesarean section or forceps delivery.

GYNAECOLOGIST

This is a doctor who has specialised in the female reproductive system.

PAEDIATRICIAN

This is a doctor who has specialised in the care of children up to the age of 16. They attend all difficult births in case the baby needs resuscitation.

HEALTH VISITOR

This is a qualified nurse who has taken further training for the care of people in the community, including midwifery experience. They work exclusively in the community, and can be approached either directly or via the family doctor. They work primarily with mothers and children up to the age of five years. Their main role is health education and preventive care.

Private services relating to antenatal care

There are many options available to the woman who can afford to pay for private antenatal and postnatal care. She may choose a home birth with a private or independent midwife. The midwife will undertake all antenatal and postnatal care and also deliver the baby. Another option is to have the baby in a private hospital or maternity unit attended by an obstetrician. Many district hospitals also offer private facilities for paying patients.

Antenatal care

THE BOOKING CLINIC

Wherever the woman decides to give birth, she will attend a lengthy interview with the midwife and the doctor will perform various tests. A bed is booked for hospital delivery for around the time the baby is due. Recognition of cultural differences and personal preferences, such as a woman's wish to be seen by a female doctor, is important and most antenatal clinics try to meet such needs. Relatives are encouraged to act as interpreters for women who understand or speak little English and leaflets explaining common antenatal procedures are usually available in different languages.

THE SIGNIFICANCE OF THE RHESUS FACTOR IN PREGNANCY

Most people are Rhesus positive; If the mother is Rhesus negative (Rh-) and the baby inherits the father's Rhesus positive (Rh+) the baby's blood can enter the mother's bloodstream during delivery – the mother's body reacts to these foreign blood cells by producing antibodies to fight them. These antibody molecules are able to cross the placenta and go back into the baby, resulting in **anaemia** or more seriously, **haemolytic disease of the newborn**, which may require an exchange blood transfusion. Prevention of this situation is by regular tests to assess the antibodies present in the maternal blood and by giving an injection of Anti-D globulin (anti-Rhesus factor) within 72 hours of the first delivery to prevent further formation of antibodies.

Table 1.2 The Booking Clinic: early pregnancy

Taking a medical and obstetric history	Medical examination
This is usually carried out by the midwife and covers the following areas: • details of the **menstrual cycle** and the date of the last period; the expected delivery date (EDD) is then calculated. • details of any **previous pregnancies**, miscarriages, or births • **medical history** – diabetes, high blood pressure or heart disease can all influence the pregnancy • **family history** – any serious illness, inherited disorders or history of twins • **social history** – the need for support at home and the quality of housing will be assessed, especially if the woman has requested a home or Domino delivery	A doctor will need to carry out the following physical examinations: • **listening to the heart and lungs** • **examining breasts** for any lumps or for inverted nipples which might cause difficulties with breast feeding • noting the presence of **varicose veins** in the legs and any swelling of legs or fingers • **internal examination** to assess the timing of the pregnancy – a cervical smear may be offered

Clinical tests

• **Height** – this can give a guide to the ideal weight; small women (under 1.5 m) will be more carefully monitored in case the pelvis is too narrow for the baby to be delivered vaginally

• **Weight** – this will be recorded at every antenatal appointment; weight gain should be steady (the average gain during pregnancy is 12–15 kg)

• **Blood pressure** – readings are recorded at every antenatal appointment, as **hypertension** or high blood pressure in pregnancy can interfere with the blood supply to the placenta

• **Urine tests** – urine is tested at every antenatal appointment for:
  - ▲ **sugar**: occasionally present in the urine during pregnancy, but if it persists may be an early sign of **diabetes**
  - ▲ **protein**: traces may indicate an infection or be an early sign of **pre-eclampsia** – a special condition only associated with pregnancy where one of the main signs is high blood pressure
  - ▲ **ketones**: these are produced when fats are broken down; the case may be constant vomiting or dieting or there may be some kidney damage

• **Blood tests** – a blood sample will be taken and screenef for:
  - ▲ **blood group**: in case transfusion is necessary; everyone belongs to one of four groups: A, AB, B or O
  - ▲ **Rhesus factor**: positive or negative (see below)
  - ▲ **syphilis**: can damage the baby if left untreated
  - ▲ **rubella immunity**: if not immune, the mother should avoid contact with the virus and be offered the vaccination after birth to safeguard future pregnancies
  - ▲ **sickle cell disease** – a form of inherited anaemia which affects people of African, West Indian and Asian descent
  - ▲ **thalassaemia** – a similar condition which mostly affects people from Mediterranean countries
  - ▲ **haemoglobin levels** – the iron content of the blood is checked regularly to exclude **anaemia**

Nutrition during pregnancy

A BALANCED DIET

Every pregnant woman hears the advice 'eating for two' but the best information available today suggests that this is not good advice. Research shows that that the quality of a baby's nutrition before birth may also lay the foundation for good health in later life. During pregnancy women should eat a well-balanced diet using the following guidelines:

> ► high in **carbohydrate** (bread, cereals, rice, pasta, potatoes)
> ► low in total **fat**. Reducing fat has the effect of reducing energy intake; therefore it is particularly important that these calories are replaced in the form of carbohydrate. Fat should not be completely avoided, however, as certain types are essential for body functioning as well as containing **fat-soluble vitamins**
> ► **protein** is also important for foetal growth and development; adequate intake is rarely a problem for healthy women in developed countries
> ► eating plenty of **fibre** will prevent constipation, and help to keep the calorie intake down

Department of Health advice is to eat according to appetite, with only a small increase in energy intake for the last three months of the pregnancy (200 kcal a day).

MICRONUTRIENTS IN PREGNANCY

During pregnancy the foetus gets all its nutrients from the mother. Pregnancy increases the requirements for a range of micronutrients, particularly **folic acid**, **calcium** and **iron**.

Folic acid is a B vitamin, which is very important throughout pregnancy, but especially in the first twelve weeks when the baby's major systems are being formed. Most doctors recommend that pregnant women take a folic acid supplement every day, as more folic acid is required than is available from a normal diet.

The Department of Health recommendations are set out in Table 1.3.

FOOD SAFETY IN PREGNANCY

Food safety issues cause pregnant women a great deal of anxiety. They can be clarified by following a few guidelines, as shown in Table 1.4.

Table 1.3 Micronutrients in pregnancy

Micronutrient	Advice
Folic acid	A diet rich in folic acid (breakfast cereals, green leafy vegetables) and a daily supplement of 400u should be taken before conception and during the first twelve weeks of pregnancy. Folic acid helps prevent neural-tube defects such as spina bifida.
Calcium	Ensure an adequate calcium intake. Good sources are dairy products (milk, cheese), tinned fish, fortified white flour (found in bread) and green leafy vegetables.
Iron	Ensure an adequate iron intake. Good sources are meat, fortified cereals and spinach. Vitamin C will increase its absorption. Avoid tea and coffee with meals containing iron.
Vitamin A	The retinol form of vitamin A should be avoided during pregnancy as it can cause physical defects in the developing embryo. Avoid retinol supplements (such as fish-liver oils), liver and liver products.

WOMEN AT RISK

Some women are at risk from poor nutrition during pregnancy. Any woman who restricts her diet for personal, religious or cultural reasons may have to take care, although well-balanced vegetarian and vegan diets should be safe. The following groups of women are potentially at risk:

- Adolescents – who have an increased nutritional requirement for their own growth as well as providing for the foetus
- Women with closely spaced pregnancies
- Women on low income
- Recent immigrants
- Women with restricted and poorly balanced diets
- Women who are very underweight or overweight
- Women who have had a previous low birthweight baby
- Women with pre-existing medical conditions, such as diabetes mellitus and food allergies

ANTENATAL CARE DURING THE MIDDLE MONTHS

Visits to the antenatal clinic, GP or community midwife will be monthly – or more often if problems are detected. On each occasion the following checks are made and recorded on The Co-operation Card, which is given to every woman to enable appropriate care to be given wherever she happens to be:

- weight
- blood pressure
- foetal heart (heard through a portable ear trumpet – a foetal stethoscope)

- urine
- fundal height (the size of the uterus)
- any oedema or swelling of ankles and/or fingers

At 28 weeks, the hospital will expect to see any mother booked in for a hospital delivery and visits are weekly in the final month of pregnancy.

A summary of the tests carried out during pregnancy is shown in Table 1.5

Health education

The midwife, doctor and health visitor are available throughout pregnancy to give advice on diet, rest, exercise or any issue causing concern; they can

Table 1.4   Food and animal safety – what to avoid in pregnancy

Infection	Food/animal sources	Comments
Listeriosis	Unpasteurised milk, ripened soft cheeses, pâté, cook/chill meals, ready-to-eat poultry. Sheep and lambs at lambing time	Flu-symptoms in the mother may cause miscarriage, stillbirth, severe illness in the baby. Avoid all sources when pregnant, and thoroughly reheat any ready-to-eat food.
Salmenollosis	Eggs, poultry and raw meet	Causes diarrhoea. Cook foods thoroughly. Prevent contamination from other foods
Toxoplasmosis	Meat (raw and undercooked), unwashed vegetables and salad, goat's milk. Cats, sheep, cat litter, soil	Flu-like symptoms in the mother may cause congenital defects in the foetus. Cook meat well, wash vegetables well. Wash hands and wear gloves when in contact with cats, cat litter, soil, sheep. Drink heat-treated milk only
Chlamydiosis	Sheep and lambs	Avoid sheep and lambs at lambing time.

Table 1.5 Screening tests in pregnancy

Name	Procedure	When	Procedure performed to assess	Comments
Chorionic Villus Sampling (CVS)	A small piece of the placenta is removed via the cervix (neck of the womb) and the cells examined	At about 8–11 weeks	• the risk of Down's syndrome, haemophilia, cystic fibrosis, thalassaemia, sickle cell disease or other genetic disorders	An eary test with results available after only 7–10 days Risk of miscarriage is higher than with amniocentesis
Amniocentesis	After an ultrasound scan a hollow needle is inserted through the abdomen to draw off a sample of amniotic fluid from inside the uterus. Foetal cells are cultured for 3–5 weeks and then examined under a microscope.	Between 14 and 18 weeks	• the presence of an extra chromosome, i.e. Down's syndrome • any missing or damaged chromosomes • missing or defective enzymes which cause metabolic disorders • if the baby is receiving enough oxygen • the baby's sex: important in identifying babies at risk of genetically linked disorders such as muscular dystrophy or haemophilia	May be offered to any woman over 35 or 38 in some hospitals) when the risk of chromosomal abnormalities is greater to any woman with a history of sex-life disorders The risk of miscarriage is estimated to be increased by 0.5–1% over the existing risk of miscarriage at this stage of pregnancy
Maternal Serum Screening Test (Bart's Test)	A blood test which measures the levels of AFP (alpha-fetoprotein) and three hormones – oestriol and two types of human chorionic gonadotrophin	At about 16 weeks	• the risk factor for neural tube defects, e.g. anencephaly and spina bifida • the risk factor for Down's syndrome	A non-invasive test useful for women considering invasive tests such as amniocentesis; it does not make a diagnosis of these conditions but indicates the level of risk involved
Triple-Plus Test	A blood test which measures levels of AFP, oestriol and human gonadotrophin, and also NAP (neutrophil alkaline phosphatase)	At about 13–16 weeks	• the risk factor for neural tube defects, e.g. anencephaly and spina bifida • the risk factor for Down's syndrome	This test is not routinely available on the NHS, but has a higher detection rate for Down's syndrome than the Barts test. When only the mother's age is used as a determining risk factor, the detection rate is 30%, whereas the Triple Plus test offers an above 80% detection rate
Ultrasound Scan	Ultrasound (sound at higher frequency than can be heard by the human ear) is used to produce pictures of the foetus in the uterus	At any stage, but usually between 16 and 18 weeks	• the size, age and position of the foetus • the position of the placenta • if there is more than one baby • if the foetus is developing normally • if there are fibroids in the womb • if the pregnancy is in the right place or ectopic	New research indicates that Down's syndrome can be detected using ultrasound. The mother would then be offered amniocentesis.

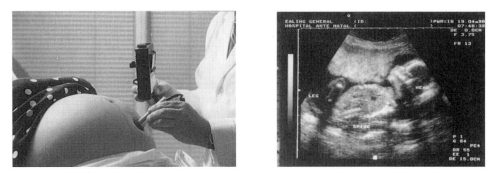

Figure 1.10a and 10b   Ultrasound examination and ultrasound of foetus

also offer advice on the current **maternity benefits** and how to apply for them.

The inverse care law operates in this area of health. The women most at risk of developing complications during pregnancy are those in poor housing, on a poor diet or whose attendance at antenatal clinics is poor or non-existent. The midwife and health visitor will be aware of the risks such factors pose for both mother and baby and will target such individuals to ensure that preventive health care, such as surveillance and immunisation reaches them.

Parentcraft classes

Childbirth preparation classes are held in hospitals, health centres, community halls or private homes. They usually welcome couples to attend from about the 28th week of pregnancy and aim to cover:

> ▶ **all aspects of pregnancy**: diet and exercise; sexual activity; how to cope with problems such as nausea, tiredness and heartburn
> ▶ **labour**: pain control methods, breathing and relaxation exercises
> ▶ **birth**: what happens at each stage and the different methods of delivery. The classes usually include a tour of the maternity unit at the hospital

They are also valuable meeting-places for discussion with other parents-to-be about all the emotional changes involved in becoming a parent. Classes may also be held for women with special needs – expectant mothers who are schoolgirls, or in one-parent families, or whose first language is not English. Some areas provide classes earlier in pregnancy (from eight to twenty weeks) or aquanatal classes where women can practise special exercises standing in shoulder-high water.

Table 1.6 A summary of genetic defects and their pattern in inheritance

Dominant gene defects	Recessive gene defects	X-linked gene defects
Tuberous sclerosis Achondroplasia Huntington's chorea Neurofibromatosis Marfan's syndrome	Cystic fibrosis Friedreich's ataxia Phenylketonuria Sickle cell anaemia Tay-Sachs disease Thalassaemia	Haemophilia Christmas disease Fragile X syndrome Muscular dystrophy (Duchenne type) Colour blindness (most types)

△ = defective gene   ○ = normal gene   ● = defective x chromosome   ⊗ = normal x chromosome   ⊗ = y chromosome

Some organisations, e.g. National Childbirth Trust (NCT), also offer parent education classes; these are usually held in small groups in the tutor's home. Fees vary according to circumstances.

Maternity rights and benefits

All pregnant women are entitled to the following rights and benefits:

- **free NHS maternity care**;
- **paid time off** for antenatal care; this care includes not only medical examinations but also parentcraft classes;
- protection against **detrimental treatment** and **unfair dismissal** because of pregnancy;
- 14 weeks **maternity leave** regardless of service;
- **free prescriptions** until the baby is one year old;
- **free dental care** until the baby is one year old;
- the right to **return to work** up to 29 weeks after the baby is born.

Other maternity benefits, such as Maternity Allowance and Maternity Benefit are administered by the Department of Social Security and are paid only to those who meet certain qualifying conditions or who are on a low income. Free milk and vitamin tokens are available to expectant mothers, and to children under five years, in families receiving Income Support.

Factors affecting physical development of the foetus

Various factors affect growth and development of the foetus. These include:

- mother's age
- the use of drugs
- premature birth
- number of pregnancies
- infection
- diet – see p. 12
- pre-eclampsia

The mother's age

The best age to have a baby from a purely physical point of view is probably between 18 and 30 years. Complications of pregnancy and labour are slightly more likely above and below these ages.

> ▶ **Younger mothers:** Under the age of 16 there is a higher risk of having a small or premature baby, of becoming anaemic and suffering from high blood pressure. Emotionally and socially, very young

teenagers are likely to find pregnancy and motherhood much harder to cope with and they will need a great deal of support.

▶ **Older first-time mothers:** First-time mothers over the age of 35 run a risk of having a baby with a chromosomal abnormality. The most common abnormality associated with age is **Down's syndrome**. A woman in her twenties has a chance of only 1 in several thousand of having such a baby, but by forty the risk is about 1 in every 110 births, and at 45 the risk is about 1 in every 30. Amniocentesis can detect the extra chromosome which results in Down's syndrome; it is usually offered routinely to women who are thirty-seven or over.

Number of pregnancies

Some problems occur more frequently in the **first** pregnancy than in later ones, for example **breech presentation**, **pre-eclampsia**, **low birth weight** and **neural tube defects**. First babies represent a slightly higher risk than second and third babies do. The risks begin to rise again with a fourth and successive pregnancies; this is partly because the uterine muscles are less efficient, but it also depends to a certain extent on age and social factors associated with larger families.

The use of drugs

Most drugs taken by the mother during pregnancy will cross the placenta and enter the foetal circulation. Some of these may cause harm, particularly during the first three months after conception. Drugs that adversely affect the development of the foetus are known as **teratogenic**.

▶ **Prescription drugs** – Drugs are sometimes prescribed by the woman's doctor to safeguard her health during pregnancy, for example antibiotics or anti-epilepsy treatment; they have to be very carefully monitored to minimise any possible effects on the unborn child.

▶ **Non-prescription drugs** such as aspirin and other painkillers should be checked for safety during pregnancy.

▶ **Alcohol** can harm the foetus if taken in excess. Babies born to mothers who drank large amounts of alcohol throughout the pregnancy may be born with **foetal alcohol syndrome**. These babies have characteristic facial deformities, stunted growth and

mental retardation. More moderate drinking may increase the risk of miscarriage, but many women continue to drink small amounts of alcohol throughout their pregnancy with no ill effects.
► **Smoking** during pregnancy reduces placental blood flow and therefore the amount of oxygen the foetus receives. Babies born to mothers who smoke are more likely to be born prematurely or to have a low birth weight.
► **Illegal drugs** such as cocaine, crack and heroin are teratogenic and may cause the foetus to grow more slowly. Babies born to heroin addicts are addicted themselves and suffer painful withdrawal symptoms. They are likely to be underweight and may even die.

Infection

Viruses or small bacteria can cross the placenta from the mother to the foetus and may interfere with normal growth and development. The first three months (the first **trimester**) of a pregnancy are when the foetus is particularly vulnerable. The most common examples are:

► **rubella** (German measles). This is a viral infection that is especially harmful to the developing foetus as it can cause congenital defects such as blindness, deafness and mental retardation. All girls in the UK are now immunised against rubella before they reach child-bearing age, and this measure has drastically reduced the incidence of rubella-damaged babies;
► **cytomegalovirus (CMV)**. This virus causes vague aches and pains and possibly fevers and poses similar risks to the rubella virus, i.e. blindness, deafness and mental retardation, but as yet there is no preventive vaccine. It is thought to infect as many as 1% of unborn babies and of those infected babies, about 10% may suffer permanent damage; and
► **toxoplasmosis**. Toxoplasmosis is an infection caused by a tiny parasite. It may be caught from eating anything infected with the parasite. This could be:
  • raw or undercooked meat, including raw cured meat such as Parma ham or salami;
  • unwashed, uncooked fruit and vegetables;
  • cat faeces and soil contaminated with cat faeces;
  • unpasteurised goat's milk and dairy products made from it.

In about one-third of cases, toxoplasmosis is transmitted to the foetus and may cause blindness, **hydrocephalus** or mental retardation. Infection in late pregnancy usually has no ill effects.

▶ **Syphilis.** This is a bacterial sexually transmitted disease (STD). It can only be transmitted across the placenta after the 20th week of pregnancy. It will cause the baby to develop congenital syphilis, or can even lead to the death of the foetus. If the woman is diagnosed as having the disease at the beginning of pregnancy (see p. 11 Booking etc) it can be satisfactorily treated before the 20th week.

Pre-eclampsia

Pre-eclampsia is a complication of later pregnancy, which can have serious implications for the well being of both mother and baby as the oxygen supply to the baby may be reduced and early delivery may be necessary. It is characterised by:

- a rise in blood pressure;
- oedema (swelling) of hands, feet, body or face due to fluid accumulating in the tissues;
- protein in the urine.

In severe cases, pre-eclampsia may lead to eclampsia, in which convulsions (seizures) can occur. This can occasionally threaten the life of both mother and baby. If pre-eclampsia is diagnosed, the woman is admitted to hospital for rest and further tests.

Premature birth

Babies who are born before the 37th week of pregnancy are now called **pre-term** babies. Around 4% of babies are born pre-term and most of them weigh less than 2500 g and are therefore also described as **low birth weight babies (**see Chapter 2 page 34). The main problems for pre-term infants are:

- **temperature control** – heat production is low and heat loss is high, because the surface area is large in proportion to the baby's weight and there is little insulation from subcutaneous fat;
- **breathing** – the respiratory system is immature and the baby may have difficulty breathing by himself because of **respiratory distress syndrome** (RDS). This is caused by a deficiency in **surfactant**, a fatty

substance which coats the baby's lungs and is only produced from about 22 weeks of pregnancy;

- **infection** – resistance to infection is poor because they have not had enough time in the uterus to acquire antibodies from the mother to protect them against infection;
- **jaundice** – due to immaturity of the liver function.

Activities relating to Chapter 1

ACTIVITY 1

Antenatal care

1 In groups, discuss the advantages and disadvantages of having a baby
   a) in hospital
   b) at home
2 a) Research the effects that smoking when pregnant may have on the developing foetus.
   b) Research the possible effects that alcohol consumption may have on the unborn baby.

ACTIVITY 2

Nutrition in pregnancy

Prepare a weekly menu plan for a pregnant woman:

a) who follows a vegan diet
b) who follows a vegetarian diet
c) who is on a limited income

Refer to a textbook on nutrition or Chapter 11 in *Child Care and Education*.

ACTIVITY 3

Research into antenatal care

Find out about the antenatal services available in your area. If possible, visit an antenatal department and write a report on the procedures that are carried out during pregnancy.

2

Birth and Care of the Newborn Child and the Mother

Birth

The process of birth: the 3 stages of labour

Towards the end of pregnancy the baby moves down the birth canal and is usually lying with head downwards. There are three signs that can be understood as a general guide that labour is starting. The woman may notice all or some of them:

STAGE 1: THE NECK OF THE UTERUS OPENS

- the 'show' – the discharge of blood-stained mucus from the vagina
- the breaking of the waters or rupture of membranes – when some amniotic fluid escapes via the vagina
- regular contractions; these are muscular contractions which may start slowly and irregularly, but become stronger and more frequent as labour progresses. They open up the cervix at the neck of the womb.

Stage 1 varies from a few hours up to 24 hours and is usually longer for the first-time mother. Once the membranes have ruptured, which may not occur until late in Stage 1, the woman should contact the midwife or

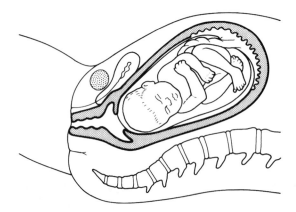

Figure 2.1   The first stage of labour

hospital as there is always a risk of infection entering the uterus if labour is very prolonged.

STAGE 2: THE BIRTH OF THE BABY

This begins when the cervix is fully dilated (open) and the baby starts to move down the birth canal and it ends when the baby is born. The contractions are very strong and the midwife encourages the mother to push with each contraction until the baby's head is ready to be born. When the baby's head stays at the entrance to the vagina, it is said to be 'crowning' and the mother is asked to 'pant' the head out. The baby will then rotate so that the shoulders are turned sideways and the rest of the body is born. Many mothers prefer to have their baby placed on their abdomen immediately, to feel the closeness and warmth.

STAGE 3: THE DELIVERY OF THE PLACENTA AND MEMBRANES

The midwife will clamp and cut the umbilical cord and the baby is labelled with the mother's name on wrist and ankle bands. Normally, the placenta

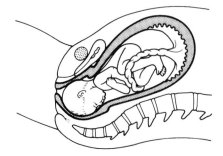 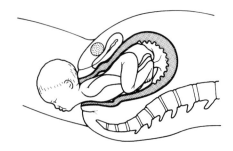

Figure 2.2   The second stage of labour

separates from the lining of the uterus within twenty minutes of the birth and is pushed out through the vagina.

Pain relief during labour

Labour is usually painful, but a thorough understanding of what is happening throughout the birth process can help to reduce the fear of the unknown that makes the body tense up and fight the contractions instead of relaxing and working with them. Different methods of pain relief include:

- **relaxation and breathing exercises** – these are taught at parentcraft classes and the support of a sympathetic partner or friend is invaluable
- **gas and air (Entanox)** – this is a mixture of oxygen and nitrous oxide ('laughing' gas); it is often offered to the mother towards the end of the first stage of labour via a rubber mask attached to the gas cylinder; it does not affect the baby and the mother is able to control her own intake
- **pethidine** – this is a strong pain-killing drug given by injection; it relaxes the muscles and makes the mother very drowsy
- **epidural anaesthetic** – this is injected into the space around the mother's spinal cord; it usually gives total pain relief and leaves the mother fully conscious
- **Transcutaneous Nerve Stimulation (TENS)** – this involves the use of electrodes which are attached externally on either side of the lower back. The electrodes are connected to a small battery-powered stimulator. The woman controls the delivery of the pulses that block the sensations of pain before they reach the brain; the technique has no adverse effects on the baby
- **Complementary therapies**: a**cupuncture and hypnosis** are also used by some women to relieve the pain of labour, but these are not generally offered within NHS units

Medical interventions in the birth process

INDUCTION

This means starting labour artificially; it involves rupturing the membranes and/or giving artificial hormones either via a vaginal pessary or by an intravenous infusion or 'drip'. It is necessary when:

> ▶ the baby is very overdue
> ▶ the placenta is no longer working properly
> ▶ the mother is ill, for example with heart disease, diabetes or **pre-eclampsia**.

EPISIOTOMY

An episiotomy is a small cut made in the perineum (the area between the vagina and the rectum) and is used during the second stage of labour:

> ▶ to deliver the baby more quickly if there are signs of foetal distress
> ▶ to prevent a large, ragged perineal tear which would be difficult to repair
> ▶ to assist with a forceps delivery.

FORCEPS DELIVERY

Forceps are like tongs that fit round the baby's head to form a protective 'cage' and are used during the second stage of labour to help deliver the head; they may be used:

> ▶ to protect the head during a **breech** delivery, that is when the baby presents bottom first
> ▶ if the mother has a condition such as heart disease or high blood pressure and must not over-exert herself
> ▶ if the labour is very prolonged and there are signs of foetal distress
> ▶ if the baby is very small or pre-term.

VACUUM EXTRACTION DELIVERY

This is an alternative to forceps, but can be used before the cervix is fully dilated; gentle suction is applied via a rubber cup placed on the baby's head.

CAESAREAN SECTION

A Caesarean section is a surgical operation done under either a general or an epidural anaesthetic; the baby is delivered through a cut in the abdominal wall. The need for a Caesarean section may be identified during pregnancy – an 'elective' or planned operation; or as an emergency:

- when **induction of labour** has failed
- when there is severe bleeding
- when the baby is too large or in too difficult a position to deliver vaginally
- in placenta praevia – when the placenta is covering the cervix
- in cases of severe foetal distress
- if the mother is too ill to withstand labour

The newborn baby or neonate

The first question usually asked by parents is 'Is he/she all right?'. The doctor and midwife will observe the newborn baby closely and perform several routine tests that will show whether the baby has any obvious physical problem (See Figures 2.3 and 2.4).

THE APGAR SCORE

This is a standard method of evaluating the condition of a newborn baby by checking five vital signs (See Table 2.1).

Skin – vernix and lanugo may still be present; milia may show on the baby's nose; black babies appear lighter in the first week of life as the pigment, melanin, is not yet at full concentration

The spine is checked for any evidence of spina bifida

The face is examined for: cleft palate – a gap in the roof of the mouth facial paralysis – temporary paralysis after compression of the facial nerve, usually after forceps delivery

Feet are checked for webbing and talipes (club foot), which needs early treatment

The head is checked for size and shape: any marks from forceps delivery are noted

Genitalia and anus are checked for any malformation

Eyes are checked for cataract – a cloudiness of the lens

Hips are tested for congenital dislocation using Barlow's Test

The neck is examined for any obvious injury to the neck muscles after a difficult delivery

The abdomen is checked for any abnormality, e.g. pyloric stenosis, where there may be obstruction of the passage of food from the stomach; the umbilical cord is checked for infection

The heart and lungs are checked using a stethoscope; any abnormal findings will be investigated

Hands are checked for webbing (fingers are joined together at the base) and creases – a single unbroken crease from one side of the palm to the other is a feature of Down's syndrome

Figure 2.3   Examination of the new-born baby by the paediatrician or family doctor

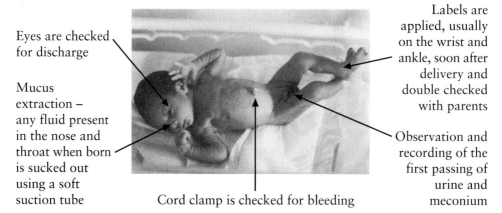

Eyes are checked for discharge

Mucus extraction – any fluid present in the nose and throat when born is sucked out using a soft suction tube

Labels are applied, usually on the wrist and ankle, soon after delivery and double checked with parents

Observation and recording of the first passing of urine and meconium

Cord clamp is checked for bleeding

Figure 2.4   Examination of the new-born baby by the midwife

Table 2.1   The Apgar score

Signs	0	1	2
Heartbeat	absent	slow below 100	fast over 100
Breathing	absent	slow irregular	good; crying
Muscle tone	limp	some limb movement	active movement
Reflex response (to stimulation of foot or nostril)	absent	grimace	cry, cough, sneeze
Colour	blue pale	body oxygenated, hands & feet blue	well-oxygenated

The Apgar score is assessed at 1 minute and 5 minutes after birth; it may be repeated at 5-minute intervals if there is cause for concern.
Interpreting the score:
10   The baby is in the best possible condition
8–9   The baby is in good condition
5–7   The baby has mild asphyxia and may need treatment
3–4   The baby has moderate asphyxia and will need treatment
0–2   The baby has severe asphyxia and needs urgent resuscitation

Most healthy babies have an Apgar score of 9, losing one point for having blue extremities – this often persists for a few hours after birth. A low score at 5 minutes is more serious than a low score at 1 minute. In hospital, the paediatrician will be notified if the score is 6 or under at 5 minutes

Special tests and immunisations soon after birth

VITAMIN K

Most hospitals routinely give all newborn babies vitamin K by injection or by mouth immediately after the birth. This increases the clotting ability of the blood and protects against a serious form of spontaneous bleeding that can occur in newborn babies.

GUTHRIE TEST

This is a blood test routinely performed on all babies on about the sixth day. A small sample of blood is taken from the baby's heel and sent for analysis of the levels of an amino acid called phenylthalanine. Babies with high levels may have an inherited condition called **phenylketonuria**. This is a very rare metabolic disorder, affecting only 1 in 10 000 babies in the UK; it can lead to brain damage and learning delay. Early diagnosis is vital and treatment involves a special formula protein diet that has to be followed throughout the person's life.

THYROID FUNCTION TEST

The Guthrie test is also used to check the baby's thyroid function. If the thyroid gland is not working properly, the baby will require treatment by the hormone thyroxine in order to ensure normal growth and development. The earlier the treatment is started the better the outlook for the child.

BCG

An injection of BCG (for protection against tuberculosis) may be given to the baby before leaving hospital; this is given in areas with many immigrants from outside Europe, North America or Australasia or if the baby is known to be in contact with tuberculosis

Features of the newborn baby or neonate

SIZE

All newborn babies are weighed and their head circumference measured soon after birth; these measurements provide vital information for professionals when charting any abnormality in development.

- **Length:** It is difficult to measure accurately the length of a neonate and many hospitals have abandoned this as a routine; the average length of a full-term baby is 50 cm.
- **Weight:** the birth weight of full-term babies varies considerably because:

- first babies tend to weigh less than brothers and sisters born later
- boys are usually larger than girls
- large parents usually have larger babies and small parents usually have smaller babies

The average weight for a full-term baby is 3.5 kg or 7.7 lbs.

- **Head circumference**: the average head circumference of a full term baby is about 35 cm.

Appearance of the newborn baby

▶ the baby will be **wet** from the amniotic fluid and she may also have some blood streaks on her head or body, picked up from a tear or an episiotomy

▶ **vernix** (literally, varnish) may be present, especially in the skin folds; it should be left to come off without any harsh rubbing of the skin

▶ **lanugo**, or fine downy hair, may be seen all over the body – especially on dark-skinned babies and those who are born pre-term

▶ **head hair**: the baby may be born with a lot of hair or be quite bald; often the hair present at birth falls out within weeks and is replaced by hair of a different colour

▶ **skin colour**: this varies and depends on the ethnic origin of the baby; at least half of all babies develop **jaundice** on the second or third day after birth which gives the skin a yellow tinge – usually no treatment is necessary

▶ **Mongolian spot**: a smooth bluish-black area of discoloration commonly found at the base of the spine on babies of African or Asian origin; it is caused by an excess of melanocytes, the brown pigment cells and is quite harmless

▶ **birthmarks**: the most common birthmark is a pinkish mark over the eyelids, often referred to as 'stork marks'; they usually disappear within a few months. Other birthmarks, such as strawberry naevus, persist for some years (See also pp. 40)

▶ the **head** is large in proportion to the body, and may be oddly shaped at first, because of:
  - **moulding**: the head may be long and pointed as the skull bones overlap slightly to allow passage through the birth canal;
  - **caput succedaneum**: a swelling on the head, caused by pressure as the head presses on the

cervix before birth; it is not dangerous and usually disappears within a few days;

- **cephalhaematoma**: a localised blood-filled swelling or bruise caused by the rupture of small blood vessels during labour; it is not dangerous but may take several weeks to subside.

▶ **fontanelles**: these are the areas where the bones of the skull have not yet fused together; they are covered by a very tough membrane and a pulse may usually be seen beating under the anterior fontanelle in a baby without much hair

▶ **milia**: sometimes called milk spots, these are small whitish-yellow spots which may be present on the face; they are caused by blocked oil ducts and disappear quite quickly

▶ **umbilical cord**: the cord is clamped and cut after birth. A stump about 2.5 cm long is left which quickly begins to shrivel and dry up; within 24 hours it is usually almost black in colour. The cord stump withers and falls off after about 5–7 days

Movements of the newborn baby

The primitive reflexes (see Figure 2.5) are thought to be a legacy from man's earliest ancestors, when such actions were essential for an infant's survival. They give an indication of the baby's general condition and the normality of her **central nervous system**. By three months these early reflexes have been replaced by voluntary movements. This can only happen when a baby learns to associate a particular action with the fulfilment of a certain need; for example, she learns that hunger is satisfied by food, which is obtained by sucking. If some of the reflexes persist after six months, this is often indicative of a neurological or learning difficulty.

▶ Babies display a number of automatic movements (known as primitive reflexes) which are reflex responses to specific stimuli; these movements are inborn and are replaced by voluntary responses as the brain takes control of behaviour; for example, the grasp reflex has to fade before the baby learns to hold objects placed in her hand. The reflexes are important indicators of the health of the **nervous system** of the baby; if they persist beyond an expected time it may indicate delay in development.

▶ **The swallowing and sucking reflexes**: when anything is put in the mouth, the baby at once sucks and swallows; some babies make their fingers sore by sucking them while still in the womb.

▶ **The rooting reflex**: if one side of the baby's cheek or mouth is gently touched, the baby's head turns towards the touch and the mouth purses as if in search of the nipple.

▶ **The grasp reflex**: when an object or finger touches the palm of the baby's hand, it is automatically grasped.

▶ **The stepping or walking reflex**: when held upright and tilting slightly forward, with feet placed on a firm surface, the baby will make forward-stepping movements.

▶ **The asymmetric tonic neck reflex**: if the baby's head is turned to one side, she will straighten the arm and leg on that side and bend the arm and leg on the opposite side.

▶ **The startle reflex**: when the baby is startled by a sudden loud noise or bright light, she will move her arms outwards with elbows bent and hands clenched.

▶ **The falling reflex (Moro reflex)**: any sudden movement which affects the neck gives the baby the feeling that she may be dropped; she will fling out her arms and open her hands before bringing them back over the chest as if to catch hold of something.

The senses of a newborn baby

SIGHT

Newborn babies can focus on faces at close range as their range of vision is about 20–25 cm. Research has shown that all young babies prefer to look at a human face above any other object (see Chapter 2 page 57). They can also distinguish colour and are more interested in three-dimensional objects than flat ones.

HEARING

Babies respond to sounds by blinking, drawing in their breath or jerking their limbs. They soon learn to recognise their mothers' voice and may stop feeding if startled by a loud noise.

SMELL AND TASTE

At ten days old, a breastfed baby can distinguish the smell of her mother's breasts from those of other women who are breastfeeding. At birth, babies show a preference for sweet tastes over salty, sour tastes; this is probably because breast milk has a fair amount of milk sugar (lactose) in it.

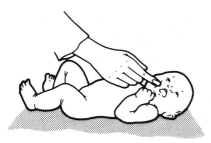

(a) Rooting reflex

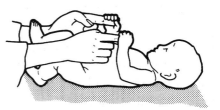

(b) Grasp reflex

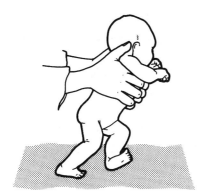

(c) Walking reflex

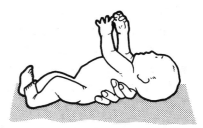

(d) Startle reflex

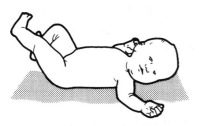

(e) Assymetric tonic neck reflex

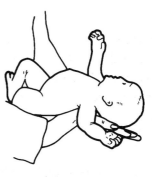

(f) Moro reflex

Figure 2.5   Reflexes of newborn baby

TOUCH

Babies explore their world with their mouths as well as with their hands and feet; they will be comforted by being cuddled or held closely. They are sensitive to touch and pain and change of position. As soon as they can, babies put things in their mouths, not to eat them but to find out more about them.

LOW BIRTH-WEIGHT BABIES

Any baby weighing up to 2.5 kg at birth, regardless of the period of gestation, is said to be of low birth-weight.

Low birth-weight babies can be divided into two categories:

- **pre-term**: babies born before 37 weeks of pregnancy;
- **light-for-dates**: babies who are below the expected weight for their gestational stage (length of pregnancy).

Some babies are both pre-term and light-for-dates. Low-birth-weight babies are at higher risk of death during the first year of life, but if they survive, most catch up with their full-size peers by school age. Those with birth-weights below 1.5 kg or who are *very* 'light-for-dates' are more likely to have lasting problems, but the rate of problems has declined as neonatal care has improved.

CAUSES

The reasons for low birth-weight are often unknown, but common factors are

- multiple births
- toxaemia of pregnancy
- a medical disorder in the mother, e.g. diabetes, heart disease, kidney infection
- drug abuse by the mother, e.g. smoking, drinking or narcotic abuse

Care of the low birth-weight baby

Most low birth-weight babies will need to be nursed in an incubator (see Figure 2.6), which is an enclosed cot with controlled temperature and humidity; the baby is usually nursed naked, sometimes lying on a sheepskin for comfort. By leaving the baby naked, the nurses are able to observe skin colour and movement without having to handle the baby. Feeding is often via a tube or a dropper until the baby has the strength to suck; extra oxygen is supplied to assist breathing.

Such an environment can seem very frightening for the parents and Special Care Baby Units (SCBUs) strive to limit any separation to a minimum. If the baby is too ill or frail to leave the incubator, the hospital will take a photograph of the baby that they can have immediately. Staff caring for neonates value the importance of early mother-baby **bonding** and will encourage parents and close family to talk to and touch the baby after

Table 2.2 A comparison of low birth-weight babies

	Light for dates	Pre-term
Gestation	Can be born at any time, even post-mature	Born before 37 weeks gestation
Birth-weight	1.500–2.500 g, regardless of gestational age	Can be any weight
Head	Often normal size – –	Appears disproportionately large firm skull bones widened skull sutures
Appearance	Wasted and obviously under-nourished 'worried little old man' look Skin dry, cracked and peeling	Skin-thin – capillaries visible Skin may be red and wrinkled Lack of subcutaneous fat Plenty of lanugo-soft, downy hair Soft, short fingernails
Behaviour	Suck and swallow reflex not effective before 32–34 weeks gestation – usually no problem	Gag, cough and swallow reflexes poor Grasp reflex often absent Moro reflex exaggerated
Problems of care	Prone to infection Needs extra warmth – incubator Greatest need is food – breast feeding is encouraged Mother-baby bonding can be more difficult	Breathing and feeding difficulties Poor temperature control – incubator High risk of infection Jaundice likely because liver is immature Mother/baby bonding can be more difficult

observing the required hygiene precautions; low birth-weight babies usually sleep more and may seem less alert than full-term babies and parents will welcome reassurance from the staff that this is normal behaviour.

Post-term babies

When pregnancy is prolonged beyond the expected date of delivery there may be problems for the baby. These result from the placenta declining in function after the 42nd week of pregnancy (NB: Full term is 40 weeks). Where the expected delivery date is accurately known, induction of labour is usually undertaken before 42 weeks. The post-term baby has the following characteristics:

- being much thinner than normal;
- having parchment-like skin which is often cracked and peeling;
- having a worried expression; and
- being alert, restless and hungry for feeds.

Treatment is similar to that for light-for-dates infants with **hypoglycaemia** presenting an additional problem.

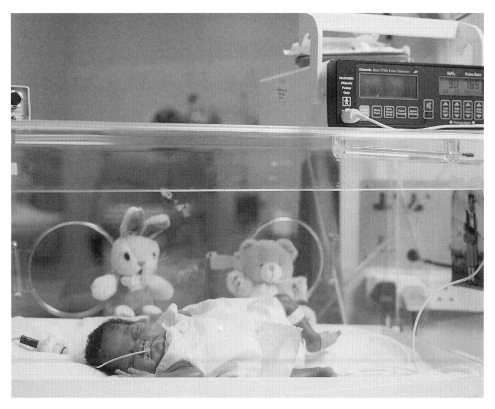

Figure 2.6 Baby in an incubator

Special Care Baby Units (SCBUs)

Special Care Baby Units are usually situated within the maternity departments of general district hospitals. They employ specially trained midwives and paediatric nurses and are designed to care for the five babies out of every hundred who require extra care that can not be provided within the normal postnatal environment.

Each hospital has its own criteria for deciding which babies need special care; usually these criteria are:

> ▶ babies born before 32 weeks
> ▶ babies weighing less than 2 kg at birth
> ▶ babies with breathing difficulties
> ▶ babies with seizures or blood disorders.

The principles of care in a SCBU are to keep the newborn baby warm and free from infection. This is achieved by expert care of babies in incubators.

Babies who are more seriously ill and who require more intensive care will be transferred to a neonatal intensive care unit.

The Neonatal Intensive Care Unit

Neonatal Intensive Care Units are situated in large regional hospitals and care for the smallest and most ill babies, using the most sophisticated technology and specialist skills. SCBUs can ensure that the sick baby receives oxygen via a face mask within the incubator; the intensive care unit can provide a **ventilator** and staff who are trained in such specialist care. Parents whose baby has had to be transferred to an intensive care unit often feel very frightened and helpless. The baby they had so eagerly anticipated is now totally at the mercy of strangers and surrounded by highly technical and noisy machinery. Often the parents feel that there is nothing they can do for their own child and the waiting is very hard to bear.

Bonding and attachment

Babies and those caring for them usually form close bonds with each other. Babies and parents who for one reason or another do not make close emotional bonds experience difficulty in stable, warm and loving relationships. As the baby is fed and held, cuddled and enjoyed, bathed and gently settled to sleep, these emotional bonds develop and deepen. Babies who find that adults respond quickly to their cries become trusting of life and well-attached in stable, warm relationships; they know that they will be fed when hungry and changed when soiled and wet and so on. The baby is already familiar with the pattern and pitch of her mother's voice from her months in the womb. There is a heightened sensitivity in the period immediately after birth, both for the mother and her baby. Medical staff recognise the importance of this sensitive period and do all they can to ensure that mother and baby are together as much as possible.

Observational studies suggest that physical contact between mother and baby encourages the attachment between them. Many midwives ask the mother if they want the baby to be delivered on to her stomach, as immediate skin-to-skin contact can be very reassuring for both mother and baby.

Common neonatal problems and disorders

JAUNDICE

Jaundice is a common condition in newborn infants that usually shows up shortly after birth. In most cases, it goes away on its own; if not, it can be treated easily. A baby has jaundice when **bilirubin**, which is produced

Figure 2.7   Mother and baby after delivery

naturally by the body, builds up faster than a newborn's liver can break it down and get rid of it in the baby's **stool**. Too much bilirubin makes a jaundiced baby's skin look yellow. This yellow colour will appear first on the face, then on the chest and stomach and finally, on the legs. Older babies, children, and adults get rid of this yellow blood product quickly, usually through bowel movements.

HOW IS JAUNDICE TREATED?

Mild to moderate levels of jaundice do not require any treatment. If high levels of jaundice do not clear up on their own, the baby may be treated with special lights (**phototherapy**) or other treatments. These special lights help get rid of the bilirubin by altering it to make it easier for the baby's liver to excrete it. Another treatment is more frequent feedings of breastmilk or formula to help pass the bilirubin out in the stools. Increasing the amount of water given to a child is not sufficient to pass the bilirubin because it must be passed in the stools.

Common skin problems in babies

A newborn baby's skin has a unique tender quality, as it has not been exposed to the environment and its ultraviolet radiation. There are certain common disorders that may affect the newborn child.

Dry skin

Some babies have dry skin that is particularly noticeable in cold weather. It can be treated by using a water-soluble cream (e.g. Unguentum Merck) instead of soap for washing and by applying vaseline to lips, cheeks or noses – the most commonly affected skin areas.

Urticaria

Neonatal urticaria are red, blotchy spots, often around a small white or yellow blister. They usually appear from around the second day and disappear within a few days. They are harmless to the baby.

Sweat rash

Sweat rash is caused by the sweat glands being immature and not allowing heat to evaporate from the skin. A rash of small red spots appears on the face, chest, groin and armpit. The baby should be kept cool and the skin kept dry; calamine lotion will soothe the itch.

Milia

Milia – often called 'milk spots' – occur in fifty percent of all newborn babies. They are firm, pearly-white pin-head sized spots which are really tiny sebaceous cysts, and are felt and seen mostly around the baby's nose. They will disappear without scarring in three to four weeks.

Peeling

Most newborn babies' skin peels a little in the first few days, especially on the soles of the feet and the palms. Postmature babies may have extra-dry skin, which is prone to peeling. Babies of Asian and Afro-Caribbean descent often have drier skin and hair than babies of European descent. No treatment is necessary.

Cradle cap

This is a type of seborrhoeic dermatitis of the scalp and is common in young babies. It is caused by the sebaceous glands on the scalp producing too much sebum or oil. The scalp is covered with white or yellowish brown crusty scales, which although they look unsightly, rarely trouble the baby. It may spread as red, scaly patches over the face, neck, armpits and eyebrows.

Sometimes it is caused by inefficient rinsing of shampoo. Treatment is by applying olive oil to the affected area overnight to soften the crusts and by special shampoo.

INFANTILE ECZEMA

Infantile eczema (or atopic dermatitis) presents as an irritating red scaly rash, usually on the baby's cheeks and forehead, though it may spread to the rest of the body. It is thought to be caused by an allergy and appears at 2–3 months. It causes severe itching, made worse by scratching. It should be treated by rehydrating the skin with short, cool baths using an unscented cleanser and frequent application of special moisturisers. If the eczema is severe, the doctor may prescribe special cortisone creams. The baby's finger nails should be kept short and scratch mittens worn. Cotton clothing should be worn and antibiotics may be used to treat any infection. It is not contagious.

Birthmarks

Most marks on the skin at birth are just temporary, but there are rare birthmarks that persist:

- **Stork marks.** These are the most common of the birthmarks, being visible in about one third of all babies. They are reddish or purple V-shaped marks usually on the back of the neck, but sometimes on the forehead or eyelids. They are harmless and always fade, becoming practically invisible after the first year.
- **Strawberry naevus.** This is a raised red area with white marks, which develops in the first week or two and grows quickly for several weeks. It usually disappears by itself and becomes smaller between two and three years. It is unusual for strawberry marks to persist beyond the age of six years. Plastic surgery to remove the mark is only required if it is on the face and causing problems for the child.
- **Port wine stain.** This is a flat irregular patch of dark reddish purple skin usually found on the face. It is much rarer than any of the other birthmarks but unfortunately does not fade or diminish with time. Treatment such as laser therapy can reduce the colour to some extent, but this is not advised in infancy.

Maintaining body temperature

From birth babies have a heat regulating mechanism in the brain which enables them to generate body warmth when they get cold. However they can rapidly become very cold for the following reasons:

> ▶ they are unable to **conserve** that warmth if the surrounding air is at a lower temperature than normal
> ▶ they have a large surface area compared to body weight
> ▶ they lack body fat, which is a good insulator.

Maternity units are always kept at a high temperature (usually about 29°C or 80°F) to allow for frequent undressing and bathing of newborn babies. At home the room temperature should not fall below 20°C (or 68°F). A pre-term or light-for-dates baby is at an even greater risk of **hypothermia**. (See page 143.)

Multiple births

Multiple pregnancies, where there is more than one baby, always need special care and supervision. Twins are the most common multiple birth, occurring in about one in 87–100 pregnancies.

IDENTICAL (MONOZYGOTIC) TWINS

Identical twins develop after one sperm has fertilised one egg; the egg splits into two and each half becomes a separate baby. Identical twins are always the same sex and they share the same placenta. (see Figure 2.8)

NON-IDENTICAL (DIZYGOTIC) TWINS

Non-identical twins develop when two sperms fertilise two different eggs, the mother's ovaries having for some reason produced two eggs at ovulation. They grow together in one womb, with two separate placentas. (See Figure 2.8) Such twins are sometimes called fraternal twins and can be the same sex or different sexes; they can be as alike or unlike as any brothers and sisters.

The chance of a woman having non-identical twins increases if she herself is such a twin or if there is a history of twins in her family.

INFERTILITY TREATMENTS AND MULTIPLE PREGNANCIES

Fertility drugs work by stimulating follicle ripening and ovulation. Sometimes they work too well and result in the ripening of more than one egg at a time. Women who are treated with fertility drugs are therefore more likely to conceive more than one child at a time.

DIAGNOSING MULTIPLE PREGNANCIES

A woman expecting more than one baby is likely to be larger than her dates would suggest and to put on more weight. Routine ultrasound scanning can

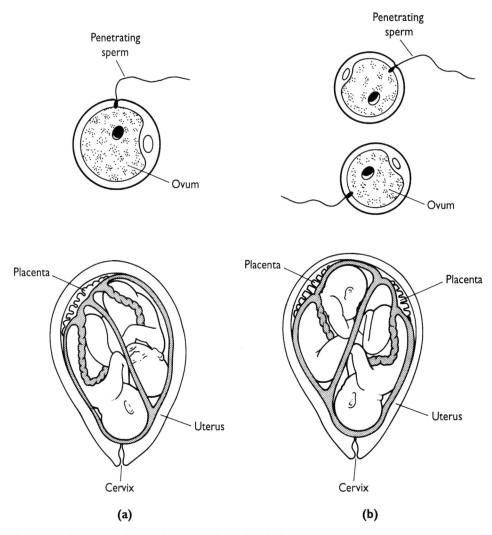

Figure 2.8 Two types of twins a) identical b) non-identical

usually detect the presence of more than one baby, unless one baby is 'hiding' behind the other.

Caring for twins and triplets

The main risk when there is more than one baby is that they will be born too early and be premature; this risk rises with the number of babies. Usually the woman expecting twins or more babies will be admitted to hospital for the birth; twins may be delivered vaginally provided both babies are in the head-down position, but triplets and quadruplets are usually delivered by Caesarean section.

FEEDING TWINS

There is no reason why mothers should not totally breastfeed twins and partly breastfeed any number of babies; however this requires great motivation and a lot of extra help and support. Bottle-feeding has the advantage of both parents or another carer being able to take part in feeding. Most mothers prepare bottle feeds for the day and keep them in the fridge, once cooled.

SUPPORT FOR PARENTS WITH TWINS AND MORE BABIES

The community midwife and health visitor will visit more frequently and will put the parents in touch with other parents in the same situation; extra help may be provided for a few weeks and arrangements are made for routine tests and immunisations to be done at home. Some parents employ a maternity nurse with neonatal experience to help them during the first few months. The La Leche League and the Twins and Multiple Births Association (TAMBA) can offer practical advice and a list of local support groups. (see addresses list). If one of the babies dies, either before birth or afterwards, the parents will require specialist bereavement counselling; the Child Bereavement Trust can offer invaluable advice and support.

PRESERVING INDIVIDUALITY

Twins who survive together should each be recognised as an individual in his or her own right. Ways of preserving individual identity are:

- not using terms such as 'the twins', but always using each child's own name;
- taking care if dressing twins and triplets alike, which will draw attention to their sameness; some twins insist on wearing identical outfits, but it is important to be aware of the disadvantages of this;
- ensuring that being 'a twin' is secondary to being 'an individual'; sharing large equipment, such as a pram or buggy, in the early years is inevitable but on birthdays, for example, two cakes could be made;
- acknowledging that each child will reach developmental milestones at different times and that individual attention from parents is worthwhile, even though this may be difficult in practice.

Postnatal care

The postnatal period is the period of six weeks from the time of the birth. For the first ten days the mother will receive help and advice from a midwife, either in hospital or at home. From ten days onwards the health visitor visits mother and baby at home. The purpose of these visits is:

- to offer advice on health and safety issues;
- to check that the baby is making expected progress;
- to offer support and advice on any emotional problems, including referring to specialist advice if necessary;
- to advise the parents to attend a baby clinic;
- to discuss a timetable for immunisations;
- to put the parent in touch with other parents locally.

Giving birth is a momentous event; everyone reacts differently and while many mothers feel an immediate rush of love and excitement, others can feel quite detached and need time to adjust. Early contact with their newborn baby is equally important for fathers as it is for mothers and learning together how to care for a newborn baby can make couples feel closer.

Postnatal depression

After giving birth a woman's hormone levels fluctuate, and this, combined with the physical and emotional exertion of childbirth, can cause new mothers to become weepy and easily upset. This feeling of mild depression is often called the **'baby blues'**. If these feelings persist longer than a few days, then it may be a more serious condition, **postnatal depression**, and the mother will need medical help.

Postnatal depression affects about 10% of women and leads to a more overwhelming feeling of inadequacy, depressed mood, and loss of energy and interest. Mothers may experience thoughts of self-harm or of harming the baby. The condition can persist for weeks or even months and may require medical treatment in the form of anti-depressive drugs.

Puerperal psychosis (or post-natal psychosis): This is a rare condition, affecting between one and two mothers per thousand births. It is a serious illness with an abrupt onset. The main features of the illness are:

- strong feelings of guilt
- mental confusion
- hallucinations
- delusions and mood disturbances
- strong feelings of despair
- hallucinations
- threats of suicide or of harm to the baby
- feelings of worthlessness

Medical treatment using anti-psychotic drugs is often needed urgently and is normally very successful. Mothers also need **counselling** and sometimes family **therapy**.

Adjusting to parenthood

Having a baby and becoming a parent is one of the greatest changes in anyone's life and a variety of emotions may be experienced. Often 'starting a family' is put off until the parents are in their late twenties or early thirties to allow each to establish their own career. The arrival of a new person in the family usually brings great happiness, but it also signals a loss of freedom and many conflicting demands. First-time mothers often find difficulty in adjusting to the completely different role of mother, when previously they may have been working away from home and not formed a network of relationships in the neighbourhood. Fathers also often find adjustment may take time, as they *want* to be involved, yet they face the conflicts between the demands of work and the increasing demands of their new family.

The number of **teenage pregnancies** has increased during the last decade. In the 1950s and 1960s it was the norm for an unmarried teenage mother to offer her child for adoption; now it is far more likely that she will care for her baby herself. The number of **lone-parent families** has also increased in recent years. There are currently around one million single-parent families in the UK. This is mainly because of the rise in divorce, but it can also arise from death of a parent, desertion – usually by the father – and from children being born outside marriage.

Activities relating to Chapter 2

ACTIVITY I

The skills of the neonate

1   Make a list of all the things a newborn baby is able to do.
2   What is the name given to movements which are automatic and inborn? Describe six such movements and explain their importance in the study of child development.

ACTIVITY 2

Bonding and attachment

1   Read about the theories of bonding and attachment proposed by John Bowlby and Mary Ainsworth (see the Bibliography at the end of this book).

2   Write a paragraph outlining why attachment may be difficult in the following situations:

> ▶ where a child is unplanned **and** unwanted
> ▶ when a baby is born with a physical disability
> ▶ when mother and baby are separated at birth, e.g. because of needing care in a Special Care Baby Unit
> ▶ when the mother experiences **postnatal depression**
> ▶ when the parents themselves have experienced emotional deprivation or abuse in childhood
> ▶ when there are social problems such as low income, poor housing or caring for several other young children.

3   For each situation, write down how bonding and attachment could be encouraged.

ACTIVITY 3

The Special Care Baby Unit

Visit a Special Care Baby Unit and answer the following questions:

1   How many babies can be looked after in the SCBU?
2   What is the ratio of staff to infants, and what are their qualifications?
3   Describe the different pieces of equipment and their uses.
4   What arrangements are made for mothers and fathers to be with their babies in the Unit?
5   What are the main problems for babies needing special care?

ACTIVITY 4

Changes in family structure

1   Find out about the different types of family structure, in particular:

> ▶ the extended family
> ▶ the nuclear family.

Describe what is meant by these terms and list the advantages and disadvantages to children of being reared in each type of family.

2 Discuss the ways in which the following factors may influence the way
in which children are reared:
a) the attitudes and beliefs of parents;
b) the culture (traditions, language, religion etc.) which is passed on
from adults to children.

3

The Developing Baby

Contents

Defining growth and development   Development of the baby in the following areas: physical, intellectual, language, emotional and social The importance of viewing the baby as a 'whole person'   Normative measurement of development   Percentile charts   Sensory development Emerging language   The nature–nurture debate   A brief overview of the major theories relating to child development   The needs of the baby Illustrated charts showing the main stages of development from birth to 18 months   Factors affecting development   Variations in development

It is important to keep in mind that even a tiny baby is a person. People grow and develop physically and intellectually, but they are whole human beings from the very start. Every child is unique – the 'average' child or the 'normal' child does not exist. Learning about child development involves studying *patterns* of growth and development and these are taken as guidelines for normal. The early years worker is ideally placed to notice when a child is not progressing according to these normal guidelines.

Defining terms

Growth

Growth refers to an increase in physical size, and can be measured by height (or length), weight and head circumference. There are two main periods of particularly rapid growth: one in the first year, the next around puberty. Different parts of the body grow at uneven rates. Growth is determined by:

- heredity
- hormones
- nutrition
- emotional influences

Development

Development is concerned with the possession of skills; **physical development** proceeds in a set order, with simple behaviours occurring before more complex skills – for example, a child will sit before she stands. The muscles involved in the act of standing require more complex involvement than those needed for sitting.

Norm

A norm is a fixed or ideal standard. Developmental norms are sometimes called milestones – the recognised pattern of physical development which it is expected that children will follow; each child will develop in a unique way and using norms helps in understanding the patterns of development while recognising the wide variation between individuals.

Holistic development of the baby

Normal development is part of a continuous process that begins in the womb. How an individual baby develops depends on two factors:

- **maturation of the nervous system**: this tends to occur in the upper body earlier than the lower parts;
- responses to external stimulation by environmental factors, particularly contact with other people.

During the first six months of life, the baby grows at a faster rate than at any other time of her life. This is not just physical growth; her understanding of the world around her and her ability to communicate are growing equally fast. Development is a complex subject and using the integrated approach may help our understanding. The following categories are widely used in the curriculum of child care courses: Physical, Intellectual (or cognitive), Language, Emotional, Social and Spiritual development.

- ▶ **Physical development** is the way in which that the body increases in skill and becomes more complex in its performance. There are two main areas:

  - **gross motor skills**: these use the large muscles in the body and include walking, running, climbing etc.;
  - **fine motor skills:** these include:
    - **gross manipulative skills** which involve single limb movements, usually the arm, for example throwing, catching and sweeping arm movements; and

- **fine manipulative skills** which involve precise use of the hands and fingers for pointing, drawing, using a knife and fork, writing, doing up shoe laces etc.

▶ **Intellectual or cognitive development** is development of the mind – the part of the brain which is used for recognising, reasoning, knowing and understanding.

▶ **Language development** – the development of communication skills through receptive speech (what a child understands), expressive speech (words she produces herself) and articulation (her actual pronunciation of words).

▶ **Emotional development** is the growth of a child's feelings about and awareness of herself; the development of feelings towards other people; and the development of self-identity and self-image.

▶ **Social development** includes the growth of the child's relationships with other people and **socialisation**, the process of learning the skills and attitudes that enable the child to live easily with other members of the community.

▶ **Spiritual development** is about the developing sense of relating to others ethically, morally and humanely.

All these areas of development are linked, and each affects and is affected by the other areas. For example, once a child has reached the stage of emotional development at which she feels secure when apart from her main carer, she will have access to a much wider range of relationships, experiences and opportunities for learning. Similarly, when a child can use language effectively, she will have more opportunities for social interaction.

Normative measurements in child development

Each child will develop in a different way; research has shown that although there is a wide variation in the chronological age (i.e. the age in years and months) at which children reach stages of development, there are recognised *patterns* of these stages. Normative measurement is concerned with **milestones** in a child's development; they show what *most* children can do at a particular stage. Mary Sheridan wrote a 'paediatric tool' – 'Children's Developmental Progress from Birth to Five Years', which aimed to familiarise all professionals working with children with the accepted milestones (or stepping stones) of development. She was particularly concerned that children with physical, mental, emotional or social disabilities were identified and fully assessed as early as possible so that appropriate help could be given to promote development.

The **value** of some means of normative measurement is:

- an early identification of children who may be experiencing difficulties;
- a comparison of a child's progress over a period of time;
- anticipating and responding appropriately to certain types of age-related behaviour, e.g. temper tantrums;
- providing reassurance that the child is developing normally;
- guiding the adult in providing for the child's developmental needs.

The **limitations** of normative measurement are:

- it may result in the child being labelled as 'below average' or as 'very bright' and expectations may be lowered or raised inappropriately;
- it may cause unnecessary anxiety when a child does not achieve milestones which are considered average for their age;
- the child's performance may be affected by a number of factors, e.g. tiredness, anxiety, illness.

Tests of normative measurement should ideally be supported by other means of assessment; **observations** are a very useful tool in the assessment of development. Professionals caring for children need to have a framework of the patterns of expected development to develop their skills in promoting health and stimulating the children's all-round development. As researchers learn more about child development, it is becoming clearer and more useful to think of a child's development as a **network** that becomes more complex as the child matures.

P	Physical
I	Intellectual/cognitive, which includes the development of symbolic behaviour
L	(a) Language and communication (b) Representation (drawings and models) (c) Play
E	Emotional
S	Social
S	Spiritual

Figure 3.1   Normative development: an updated PILESS framework

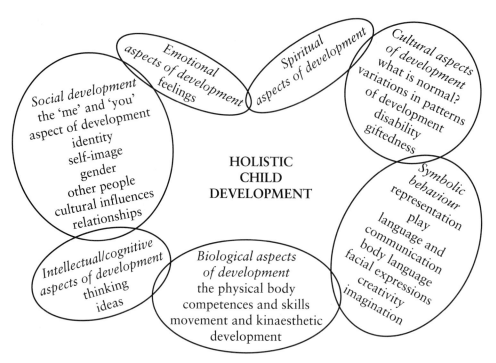

Figure 3.2 Normative development: a holistic scheme of child development

Growth charts

The latest growth charts (published in 1994) indicate the fact that children in many countries have become taller and heavier at all ages; they also mature earlier and so stop growing at an earlier age. These charts may be used to compare the growth pattern of an individual child with the normal range of growth patterns typical of a large number of children of the same sex; they are used to plot height, weight and head circumference (see Chapter 3, Figure 3.3):

- the 50th centile (or percentile) is the median: it represents the middle of the range of growth patterns;
- the 10th centile is close to the bottom of the range; if the height of a child is on the 10th centile, it means that in any typical group of 100 children, 90 would measure more and 9 would measure less;
- the 90th centile is close to the top of the range; if the weight of a child is on the 90th centile, then in any typical group of 100 children, 89 would weigh less and 10 would weigh more.

If a baby is born pre-term the birth weight must be recorded to allow for the number of weeks of prematurity. A baby born at thirty-five weeks, for example, will have her birth weight recorded at thirty-five weeks. When that baby is eight weeks old the measurement for weight at that time will be three weeks after the expected delivery date (EDD), i.e. $35 + 8 = 43$. The full term delivery time is 40 weeks and similar adjustments for pre-term infants usually continue for their first year.

Physical development

BODY SHAPE

As a child grows, the various parts of the body change in shape and proportion as well as increasing in size; the different body parts also grow at different rates e.g. the feet and hands of a teenager will reach their final adult size before the body does. At birth, a baby's head will be about $\frac{1}{4}$ of the total length of the body, whereas at seven years old, the head will be about $\frac{1}{6}$ of total length.

The pattern of development

Babies development follows a pattern:

> ► **From simple to complex**
> *Example*: a baby will walk before she can skip or hop.
> ► **From head to toe:** physical control and co-ordination begins with the baby's head and works down the body through the arms, hands and back and finally to the legs and feet.
> *Example*: a baby has to learn to sit before she can learn to stand or walk
> ► **From inner to outer**
> *Example*: a child can co-ordinate her arms using gross motor skills to *reach* for an object before she has learned the fine motor skills necessary to pick it up.
> ► **From general to specific**
> *Example:* a young baby shows pleasure by a massive general response (eyes widen, legs and arms move vigorously etc.); an older child shows pleasure by smiling or using appropriate words and gestures.

Sensory development

Sensation is the process by which we receive information through the senses:

- vision
- smell
- taste
- hearing
- touch
- proprioception

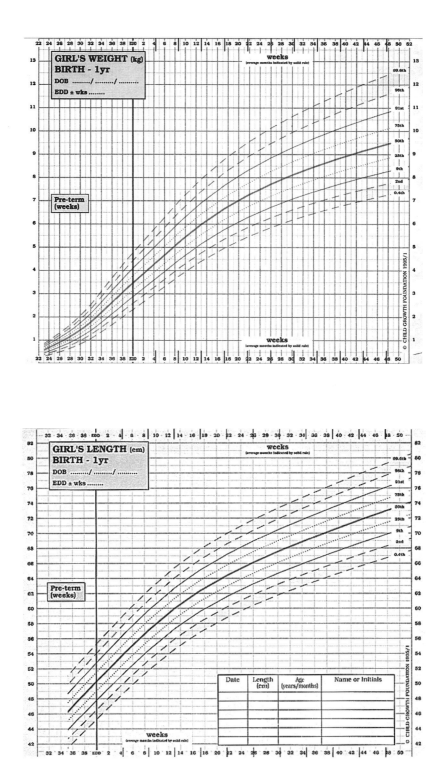

Figure 3.3   Child growth charts (weight and length – 0–1 year)

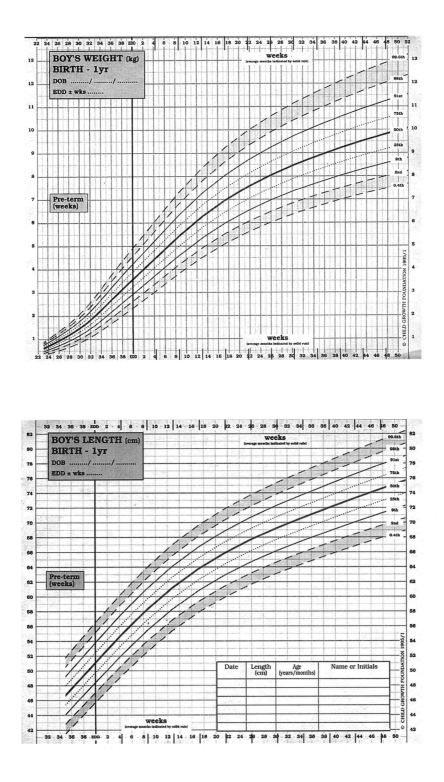

Figure 3.3   *continued*

Perception is making sense of what we see, hear, touch, smell and taste. Our perception is affected by previous experience and knowledge and by our emotional state at the time. There are therefore wide variations in the way different individuals perceive the same object, situation or experience.

Visual development

A newborn baby's eyes are barely half the size of an adult's, and although they are structurally similar, they differ in two ways:

1 their **focus** is fixed at about 20 cm, which is the distance from the baby to her mother's face when breastfeeding. Anything nearer or farther away appears blurred. She will remain shortsighted for about four months.
2 The **response to visual stimuli is slower** in babies because the information received by the eye takes longer to reach the brain via the nervous pathway.

Figure 3.4   Baby breast feeding

A newborn baby is only able to poorly fix her eyes upon objects and follow their movement. Head and eye movement is also poorly co-ordinated; in the first week or two, the eyes lag behind when the baby's head is turned to one side, a feature known by paediatricians as the 'doll's eye phenomenon'. Research has shown that babies prefer looking at:

- **patterned** areas rather than plain ones;
- anything which resembles a **human face**. Babies will actually search out and stare at human faces during their first two months of life;
- **brightly coloured** objects.

By around four months a baby can focus on both near and distant objects and her ability to recognise different objects is improving steadily. By six months the baby will respond visually to movements across the room and will move her head to see what is happening. By one year her eye movements are smoother and she can follow rapidly moving objects with the eyes (a skill known as **tracking**). A squint is normal

The development of hearing

Newborn babies are able to hear almost as well as adults do. Certain rhythmic sounds seem to have a special soothing effect on babies; the drone of a vacuum cleaner or hairdryer is calming. The sound of a human voice evokes the greatest response and the rhythms of lullabies have been used for centuries in all cultures to help babies to sleep, or to comfort them. Babies can recognise their own mother's voice from the first week and can distinguish its tone and pitch from those of other people.

Sudden changes in noise levels tend to disturb very young babies and make them jump. From about six months, a baby will learn to recognise and distinguish between different sounds; for example, the sound of a spoon in a dish will mean food is on its way. Babies can also discriminate between cheerful and angry voices and respond in kind.

The development of smell, taste and touch

The senses of smell and taste are closely linked. If our sense of smell is defective, for example because of a cold, then our sense of taste is reduced.

Babies as young as one week old who are breastfed are able to tell the difference between their own mother's smell and other women's smells. From birth babies are also able to distinguish between the four basic tastes – sweet, sour, bitter and salty.

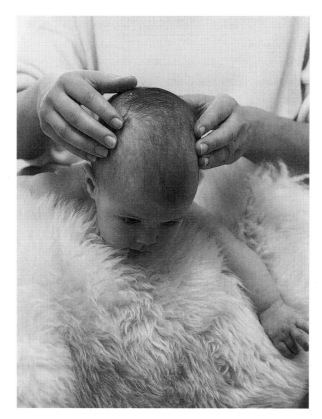

Figure 3.5 Baby being massaged

The sense of touch is also well developed in infancy as can be demonstrated by the primitive reflexes (see page 33). Babies seem to be particularly sensitive to touches on the mouth, the face, the hands, and the soles of the feet and the abdomen. Research has shown that babies would rather be stroked than fed. (See page 80 Activity: baby massage.)

Proprioception is the sense which tells the infant the location of the mobile parts of his body (e.g. his legs) in relation to the rest of him.

Sensory deprivation

A congenitally blind baby (i.e. a baby who is born blind) will develop a more sophisticated sense of touch than a sighted baby will, although they both start life with the same touch potential. As the sense of touch develops, so the area of the brain normally assigned to touch increases in size for the blind baby, and the area of the brain normally assigned to sight decreases.

Similarly, in a congenitally deaf baby, the part of the brain that normally receives auditory stimuli is taken over by the visual input from sign language.

Cognitive and language development

During childhood the brain grows rapidly. Every brain cell – or **neuron** – that the person will ever use throughout life is present at birth; the baby's experiences of the world are vital to the restructuring of the brain, which forms increasingly specialised pathways to control different behaviours. By the age of one year the baby's brain will have reached three-quarters of its adult size and up until middle childhood the two **hemispheres** of the brain become more interconnected and specialised. **Cognitive** – or intellectual – development refers to the development of the parts of the brain concerned with perceiving, reasoning and acquiring knowledge and understanding. Physical and cognitive development take place side by side; from the moment of birth a child is absorbing knowledge about the environment through the senses of sight, sound, touch, smell and taste. Cognitive development and **language development** are essential components of the **learning process** and go along together. Progress in one area affects progress in the other. Theories of human development often focus on the central issues of nature and nurture.

The nature/nurture debate

Developmental psychologists tend to emphasise either:

- **nature**, the idea that intelligence, learning and personalities are fixed from the moment of birth, that is, that they are *inherited* characteristics; or
- **nurture**, the idea that intelligence, learning and emotional and social behaviour is a product of experience. That is, that they are *acquired* characteristics.

Jean Piaget (1896–1980)

Jean Piaget believed that babies are born with the ability to adapt to and learn from the environment; their innate mental processes are basic patterns of actions – Piaget called them **schemas**. The reflexes of a newborn baby (see page 33) are primitive schema, which provide a framework for action that are later transformed into new schemas through the process of **adaptation**.

The process of adaptation

Piaget maintained that the method of developing **schemas** involves the following processes:

▶ **assimilation:** During assimilation, the child takes in new information and tries to make it conform to what is already known from previous experiences;
   Example: Sucking is a primitive schema, present as a reflex in the newborn baby; when lightly touched on the cheek by a nipple, the baby will turn and start sucking on the nipple. Later, the baby may find his thumb or finger touching his cheek – because it feels not unlike the nipple, the child will start sucking on it. (The schema itself changes little but now includes the possibility of a new object.)

▶ **Accommodation**: Accommodation is the adjustment which takes place in one's understanding of something following new experiences; the schema adapts itself, or **accommodates** to the new situation.
   Example: When babies encounter another object, e.g. a blanket, they may try to suck it; however, as the blanket is very unlike the nipple or thumb, it is not assimilated into the sucking schema. Babies then make some **accommodation;** they will modify the existing sucking schema to take account of the new experience, perhaps by choosing one corner of the blanket or by only sucking the smooth satin binding.

▶ **Equilibration:** This third part of the adaptation process involves a periodic re-structuring of schemas into new structures; children are motivated to develop schemas by the process of equibrilation, as it restores equilibrium – or balance – and so reduces tension.
   Example: A child has a pet dog called Max. At first, he may think that all dogs are called Max – or even all cats. He gradually learns that dogs are similar but different from cats. He also learns that other people's dogs have different names, and that although dogs and cats are different, they are both animals. His concept of dogs and animals continues to develop through this process of
   assimilation → disequilibrium → accommodation → equilibrium.

Piaget and child development

Piaget maintained that the young baby's mind works very differently from an adult's, and that the child's thinking passes through a sequence of

Table 3.1   Piaget's substages of sensorimotor development

Substage 1 Birth–6 weeks	**Reflex schemas exercised** The reflexes present at birth provide the initial connection between infants and their environments. Involuntary rooting, sucking, grasping and looking all produce stimulation in addition to responses to stimuli. *Example:* when infants suck, they experience tactile pressure on the roof of the mouth; this stimulates further sucking, which produces more tactile pressure, and so on.
Substage 2 6 weeks–4 months	**Primary circular reactions** This is the repetition of actions which are pleasurable in themselves. Existing reflexes are extended in time or are applied to new objects. Such actions are termed primary because they are centred on the baby's own body; they are termed circular because they lead only back to themselves. *Example:* infants may suck between feeds, or may suck their thumbs. They may also wave their hands about and kick their feet, purely for the pleasure experienced through such actions.
Substage 3 4–8 months	**Secondary circular reactions** Infants begin to realise that objects are more than extensions of their own actions; their focus is on objects external to themselves. Infants will repeat actions that produce interesting changes in the environment. *Example:* when babies make a noise and their mother responds, they will repeat that noise. Similarly, a baby may enjoy shaking a rattle or bell.
Substage 4 8–12 months	**Coordination of secondary circular reactions** Infants combine actions to achieve a desired effect; such coordinated effort is seen as the earliest form of true problem-solving. Infants now understand that objects have an existence independent of themselves. *Example:* infants will knock a pillow away in order to reach for a desired toy.
Substage 5 12–18 months	**Tertiary circular reactions** Infants begin to 'experiment'; they try out new ways of playing with or manipulating objects in order to see what the consequences will be. Improved motor skills also aid wider exploration of the child's environment. *Example:* Piaget's son, Laurent, aged 10 months, is lying in his cot: 'He grasps in succession a celluloid swan, a box etc., stretches out his arm and lets them fall … Sometimes he stretches out his arm vertically, sometimes he holds it obliquely, in front of or behind his eyes, etc. When the object falls in a new position (e.g. on his pillow), he lets it fall two or three times more on the same place, as though to study the spatial relations; then he modifies the situation.'
Substage 6 18–24 months	**Beginnings of symbolic representation** Infants use images, perhaps words or actions, to stand for objects. They indicate that they can carry out actions mentally and think about objects that are not present. This substage is really the beginning of the next major stage: pre-operational thought. *Example:* the child will search for a hidden object, certain that it exists somewhere (object permanence).

consecutive changes on the path to adulthood. All cognitive development proceeds as a result of the child performing **operations** on his environment. An operation may be mental or physical; it is anything the child does which has an effect on his environment.

Object permanence

Piaget believed that there are a series of steps in the child's emerging understanding of object permanence. Object permanence is the recognition that an object continues to exist even when it is temporarily out of sight. The first sign that the baby is developing object permanence comes at about two months of age. If you show a toy to a child of this age, put a screen in front of the toy, and then remove the toy – the child shows a surprised reaction, as if she knew that something should still be there. However, babies of this age show no signs of searching for a dropped toy or one that may have disappeared beneath a blanket.

Vygotsky, Bruner and scaffolding

Jerome Bruner is a psychologist who, taking some ideas from Lev Vygotsky, believes that adults can be a great help to children in their thinking. During a book-reading session with the child, the 'tutor' or parent will demonstrate the process by:

a) engaging the child's attention e.g. by saying 'Look';
b) simplifying the task by focusing on one question: 'What's that?';
c) maintaining motivation by encouraging any responses;
d) giving information about objects in the book: 'It's an X';
e) giving appropriate feedback: 'That's right, it's an X' and encouraging repetition by the child.

Language development from birth to 18 months

Language is the basis of all social communication and sets human beings apart from the rest of the animal world. All children develop at slightly different rates, but the *sequence* of development is the same in all children.

The stage of emerging language is the stage *before* the first word used with meaning – including crying, cooing, babbling, pointing and smiling. See Table 3.2.

Figure 3.6   Baby and mother reading

Baby Talk Register (BTR)

Many adults talk differently to young children from the way they speak to adults. Baby Talk Register has the following features:

- It is spoken in a higher-pitched voice.
- Sentences are shorter and key words are emphasised.
- Speech is slower and sentences use simple grammar.
- It is highly repetitive; the same sentences, or variations of the same sentences, may be used over and over again, e.g. 'Where is the teddy? Can you see the teddy? There is the teddy!' The adult often repeats the child's sentences, sometimes correcting the grammar in the repetition; a child using telegraphic speech, e.g. 'Daddy car' may obtain the response 'Yes, Daddy has gone to work in his car'.
- The vocabulary is limited to words that the child will understand and tends to refer to concrete objects that are immediately present.
- Diminutive or reduplicative words are common, e.g. 'doggie' or 'choo-choo'. English makes particular use of a 'y/ie' ending, and similar forms are found in other languages, e.g. Japanese – '-ko.'
- There is a high frequency of question forms and many sentences end on a higher intonation, e.g. 'yes?' and 'all right?'

Although BTR, or something resembling BTR, exists in most cultures and contexts, it is not found in every society. Research has shown that even

Table 3.2   The stage of emerging language

0–8 weeks: Basic biological noises

Expression: Over the first few weeks of life, a baby's vocal sounds directly reflect their biological state and activities. States of hunger, pain or discomfort that cause fussing and crying are known as **reflexive noises**. Bodily actions which are concerned with survival – breathing, eating and excreting – give rise to a wide range of **vegetative noises**, such as sucking, swallowing, coughing and burping. It is often difficult to determine the nature of a baby's cries during this period.
Reception: The baby will turn her head to regard a nearby speaker and react appropriately to meaningful sounds e.g. when her meal is being prepared. Just as very young infants show a preference for human faces, so they are able to distinguish and show a preference for listening to human speech.

Two to four months: Cooing and laughing.

Expression: Cooing sounds develop alongside crying, but are produced when the baby is in a settled state. These cooing sounds are quieter, lower pitched and more musical than crying; they usually consist of a short, vowel-like sound preceded by a consonant-like sound made toward the back of the mouth. Later in this period, cooing sounds are strung together – often 10 or more at a time. Some of these sequences (such as 'ga' and 'gu' begin to resemble the syllables of later speech. At around four months, the first throaty chuckles and laughs come out.
Reception: The baby can now **localize** sounds and pays interested attention to nearby meaningful sounds, particularly familiar voices.

Five to seven months: Vocal play

Expression: There is a lot of variation in the sounds produced during vocal play. The sounds are much steadier and longer than those of cooing. Most voice sequences last over one second and are usually at a high pitch level; they consists of consonant and vowel-like sequences that are often repeated. There seems to be a strong element of practice in the vocal activities of this period.
Reception: The baby now begins to respond in a discriminating way to emotional overtones in the speech of familiar adults (i.e. soothing or annoyed).

Six months to one year: Babbling

Expression: A similar set of sounds is used in babbling but the sounds are much less varied. Sequences such as 'bababa' are common and are termed **reduplicated babbling** because of the repeated use of the same consonant sound. This later develops into **variegated babbling**, in which consonants and vowels change from one syllable to the next (e.g. 'adu'). Whilst babbling appears to have no meaning, the rhythm and syllable length often resemble the words of later speech.
Reception: The baby becomes increasingly competent at localizing sounds from greater distances. Towards the end of this period, babies imitate adult's playful sounds, including occasional word forms. Babies now know and turn to their own name.

9–18 months: Melodic utterances, holophrastic speech

Expression: Towards the end of the child's first year, variations in melody, rhythm and tone of voice become a major feature of speech. Individual syllables are increasingly used with a fixed melody or intonation, producing **'proto-words'**, where the sounds are clear but the meaning is often unclear. These are the first real signs of language development, and children growing up in different language environments begin to sound increasingly unlike each other. At around 15 months the child will spontaneously use single words in the correct context, and often points to familiar objects or to things that he wants. Often one word is used to mean different things; this is called **holophrase**, e.g. 'car' may mean 'give me the car' or 'look at the car'. By 18 months the child may echo the last words spoken by an adult, – this is called **echolalia**, and may use **pivot words**: words which have a fixed position in the child's speech e.g. Mummy gone, car gone, more milk, more biscuit Children also often use **jargoning**, which is babbling with the sound of adult speech; this is sometimes called scribble talk – to the listener it sounds as if the child is having a conversation.
Reception: The child now turns to another's voice appropriately and may obey simple instructions. At this stage, children will also recognize words for several common objects and activities.

newborn infants can discriminate between Baby Talk Register and adult-directed speech, and that they *prefer* to listen to BTR. This may be due to the lilting, musical quality of the speech patterns.

Emotional and social development

Emotional development involves the development of self-image and identity, the ways in which children make sense of emotions in themselves and the development of feelings towards other people. Social development involves the growth of the child's relationship with others, the development of social skills and **socialisation**. It is impossible to isolate emotional and social development from any other areas of development; both these aspects of human development are inextricably bound up with the other aspects of cognitive, language, spiritual and moral development. For the purposes of understanding the 'whole child', it is useful to study these aspects of development in manageable sections and from the viewpoint of the relevant theoretical perspectives.

The emergence of emotions

Babies have feelings and emotions from the moment they are born; the word 'emotion' derives from a Latin verb meaning 'to move, excite, agitate'. Emotion is often referred to as 'affect' by psychologists and is an important part of human psychological behaviour.

By expressing emotions, we can:

* **communicate** to other people how we are responding to certain situations;
  Example: a newborn baby will cry to express hunger or discomfort;
* **motivate** – by alerting us to particular information in the environment, and preparing us to respond in certain ways;
  Example: the 'fight' or 'flight' reaction to a perceived threat enables us to cope effectively.

The behaviourist John B. Watson, writing in 1930, described three primary emotions felt by newborn infants – fear, anger and love:

1 **fear** – fear is aroused by threatening stimuli and the baby's response is shown by crying and clutching;
2 **anger** – anger is provoked by the blocking of the baby's activities and he responds by stiffening his body and holding his breath; and

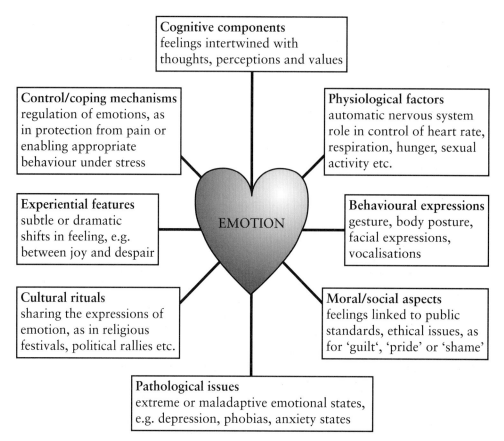

Figure 3.7   The dimensions of emotion

3 **love** – love is aroused by soothing stimulation, e.g. cooing, and the baby responds by smiling.

Not all psychologists agree that newborn babies feel such emotions. Although facial expressions have universal meanings for adults, young babies lack the maturity of higher brain mechanisms to be able to convey the same meanings through facial expression.

Stages of development and the role of the carer in promoting development

The needs of the young baby

Every baby depends completely on an adult to meet all their needs, but the manner of meeting those needs will vary considerably according to family circumstances, culture and the personalities of the baby and the caring adult. To achieve and maintain healthy growth and development, (that is physical, intellectual and emotional), certain basic needs must be fulfilled:

- food
- shelter, warmth, clothing
- cleanliness
- fresh air and sunlight
- sleep, rest and activity
- protection from infection and injury

Table 3.3 Birth to 4 weeks

Gross motor skills	Fine motor skills
Baby lies supine (on her back) with head to one side. When placed on her front (the prone position) she lies with head turned to one side, and by one month can lift her head. If pulled to sitting position, her head will lag, her back is rounded and her head flops forward.	She will turn her head towards the light and stare at bright shiny objects. She is fascinated by human faces and gazes attentively at her carer's face when fed or held. Her hands are usually tightly closed. She is startled by sudden noise, but by one month may be soothed by particular music.
Cognitive and language	**Emotional and social**
Baby responds to sounds, especially familiar voices. She quietens when picked up. She makes eye contact and cries to indicate need. She may move her eyes towards the direction of sound.	The first smile in definite response to her carer is usually aroun d 5–6 weeks. She often imitates facial expressions (e.g. tongue-pulling) She uses total body movements to express pleasure at bathtime or when being fed. She enjoys feeding and cuddling.
THE ROLE OF THE CARER IN STIMULATING DEVELOPMENT	
Promoting physical development: Encourage the baby to lie on the floor and kick and experiment safely with movement. Provide an opportunity for her to feel the freedom of moving without a nappy or clothes on. Always support the baby's head when playing with her as her neck muscles are not strong enough to control movement. Use bright colours in furnishings. Provide a mobile over the cot and/or the nappy-changing area. Feed on demand and talk and sing to her.	**Promoting cognitive, emotional & social development:** Provide plenty of physical contact and maintain eye contact. Talk lovingly to her and give her the opportunity to respond. Introduce her to different household noises. Provide contact with other adults and children. Encourage bonding with main carer by enjoying the relationship. Expect no set routine in the first few weeks. Pick her up and talk to her face-to-face.

It is difficult to separate these basic needs in practical care, as they all contribute to the holistic development of a healthy baby. Secondary needs are equally important when considering the overall development and wellbeing of the baby. These are:

1 the need for love;
2 the need for security;
3 the need for new experiences;
4 the need for praise and recognition;
5 the need for responsibility.

Table 3.4 From 4–8 weeks

Gross motor skills	Fine motor skills
Baby can now turn from her side to her back. She can lift her head briefly from the prone position. Her arm and leg movements are jerky and uncontrolled. There is head lag if she is pulled to a sitting position. She is starting to take her fist to her mouth.	Baby turns her head towards the light and stares at bright shiny objects. She will show interest and excitement by facial expression and will gaze attentively at her carer's face whilst being fed. She will open her hand to grasp your finger.
Cognitive and language	**Emotional and social**
Baby recognises her carer and familiar objects. Beginning to repeat enjoyable movements, e.g. thumb sucking. She makes non-crying noises such as cooing and gurgling. Her cries become more expressive. She looks in the direction of sounds.	She smiles in response to adult. Parent/carer is becoming more aware of the baby's temperament, which may be, e.g. placid or excitable. She enjoys sucking. She turns to regard nearby speaker's face.
THE ROLE OF THE CARER IN STIMULATING DEVELOPMENT	
Promoting physical development: Use a special supporting infant chair so that the baby can see adult activity. Let her kick freely without nappies. Massage her body and limbs during or after bathing. Use brighly coloured mobiles and wind chimes over her cot and/or changing mat. Let her explore different textures. Light rattles and toys strung over her pram or cot will encourage focusing and coordination.	**Promoting cognitive, emotional & social development:** Talk to and smile with the baby. Sing while feeding or bathing her – allow her time to respond. Learn to distinguish her cries and to respond to them differently. Tickling and teasing her may induce laughter. Talk to her and hold her close.

1 The need for love

Children need a stable, continuous, reliable and loving relationship with their parents (or permanent parent-substitutes), whom themselves take pleasure from a rewarding relationship with one another. John Bowlby's studies of **attachment** emphasise the importance of the child's need for love and security. His theory of maternal deprivation states that:

Table 3.5 8 to 12 weeks

Gross motor skills	Fine motor skills
When lying supine, baby's head is in a central position. She can now lift her head and chest off the bed in the prone position, supported on forearms. There is almost no head lag in the sitting position. Her legs can kick vigorously, both separately and together. She can wave her arms and bring her hands together over her body.	Baby moves her head to follow adult movements. She watches her hands and plays with her fingers. Clasps and unclasps hands and joins hands at midline and takes them to her mouth. Tries to pick up toy using both hands. She holds a rattle for a brief time before dropping it.
Cognitive and language	**Emotional and social**
Baby is still distressed by sudden loud noises. Taking greater interest in surroundings. Laughs and vocalises with increasing tone and intensity. She often sucks or licks her lips when she hears sound of food preparation. She shows excitement at sound of approaching footsteps or voices. Conversational babble.	She shows enjoyment at caring routines such as bathtime. She responds with obvious pleasure to loving attention and cuddles. She fixes her eyes unblinkingly on her carer's face when feeding. She stays awake for longer periods of time; 70% of babies sleep through the night.
THE ROLE OF THE CARER IN STIMULATING DEVELOPMENT	
Promoting physical development: Place the baby in a supporting infant chair so that she can watch adult activity. Encourage her to kick without nappies. Massage or stroke her limbs when bathing or if using massage oil. Use brightly coloured mobiles and wind chimes to encourage focusing at 20 cm. Place a rattle in her hand and attach objects which make a noise when struck above the cot.	**Promoting cognitive, emotional & social development** Enjoys listening to nursery rhymes. Talk sensibly to her and immitate her sounds to encourage her to repeat them. Holding her close and talking lovingly will strengthen the bonding process. Encourage contact with other adults and children. Respond to her needs and show enjoyment in caring for her.

> ▶ The first five years of life are the most important in a person's development. (This had already been proposed by Freud and other psychodynamic theorists.)
> ▶ A child's relationship with its parents (in particular with the mother) has an enormous effect on the child's overall development.
> ▶ Separation from a parent, particularly from the mother, is a major cause of psychological distress or trauma.
> ▶ Such separation and consequent psychological trauma in childhood have long-lasting effects on the overall development of the child.
> ▶ The attachment bond is **monotropic** – this means that it is established between the infant and one other person. Other relationships may be formed, but these differ in quality from the one

Table 3.6 4–5 months (16–20 weeks)

Gross motor skills	Fine motor skills
Baby has good head control. She is beginning to sit with support and can roll over from her back to her side. She is beginning to reach for objects. When supine, she plays with her own feet. She holds her head up when pulled to a sitting position.	She is beginning to use **palmar grasp**. She can transfer objects from hand to hand. She is very interested in all activity. Everything is taken to her mouth. She moves her head around to follow people and objects.
Cognitive and language	**Emotional and social**
The baby recognises her bottle or other familiar objects. She laughs and squeals with pleasure. She reacts to tones of voice; she is upset by an angry tone and cheered by a happy tone.	The baby enjoys attention and being with others. She shows trust and security. She has recognisable sleep patterns.
THE ROLE OF THE CARER IN STIMULATING DEVELOPMENT	
Promoting physical development: Practise sitting with the baby on the carer's knee. Play rough and tumble games on the bed. Play bouncing games on the carer's knee to songs. Offer rattles and soft, squashy toys to give a variety of textures. Home-made toys e.g. transparent plastic containers with dried peas inside or empty cotton reels tied together provide interest. **NB:** Check lids are secure and **always** supervise play	**Promoting cognitive, emotional & social development** Continue talking to the baby, particularly in response to her own sounds. Provide different toys with a range of textures and sound. Sing nursery rhymes combined with finger play, e.g. 'This little piggy . . .' Give her the opportunity to find out things for herself and to begin to choose play activities. Encourage playing alone and in the company of other children. Waterproof books in the bath give a lot of pleasure.

between the infant and the primary caregiver and do not have the same impact on later social and emotional development.

▶ Attachment is a highly evolved system of regulation that normally

Table 3.7 6–9 months

Gross motor skills	Fine motor skills
The baby can roll from front to back. She may attempt to crawl but will often end up sliding backwards. She may grasp her feet and place them in her mouth. She can sit without support for longer periods of time. She may 'cruise' around furniture and may even stand or walk alone.	The baby is alert to people and objects. She is beginning to use pincer grasp with thumb and index finger. She transfers toys from one hand to the other. She looks for fallen objects. Everything is explored by putting it in her mouth.

Cognitive and language	Emotional and social
The baby understands signs, e.g. bib means that food is coming. She also understands 'up' and 'down' and makes appropriate gestures, e.g. raising her arms to be picked up. She babbles tunefully with lots of imitation. She can imitate, clap and play peek-a-boo. From 8 to 9 months babies show that they know objects exist even when they have gone out of sight (object permanence – see page 000)	The baby can manage to feed herself with her fingers. She's now more wary of strangers. She offers toys to others. She shows distress when her mother leaves. Babies are now more aware of other people's feelings. They cry if brother cries, for example and laugh with others. This is called recognition of an emotion; it does not mean that they are really laughing or crying.

THE ROLE OF THE CARER IN STIMULATING DEVELOPMENT	
Promoting physical development: Encourage confidence and balance by placing toys around the sitting baby. Make sure furniture is stable and has no sharp corners when baby is using it to pull herself up by. Encourage mobility by placing toys just out of baby's reach. Encourage visual awareness by providing varied experiences. Small objects, which must be safe if chewed by the baby, will encourage the pincer grasp (small pieces of biscuit are ideal, but **always** supervise) Build a tower of bricks with her and watch her delight when they all fall down. Look at picture books together and encourage her to point at objects with you.	**Promoting cognitive, emotional & social development:** Respond to the baby pointing at objects by naming them. Talk to her about everyday things. Widen her experiences by going on outings which include animals. Imitate animal sounds and encourage her to copy you. Allow plenty of time for play. Provide simple 'musical instruments' e.g. xylophone or wooden spoon and saucepan. Use a safety mirror for the baby to recognise herself.

develops during the first year of life to produce a **dynamic equilibrium** between the mother-child pair.

▶ There exists a **critical** (or **sensitive**) **period** for attachment formation. Bowlby thought that the period between 6 months and 3 years was critical for attachment formation.

▶ **Unconditional love:** The basic feature of parental love is that the child is valued *unconditionally*. The giving of this love does not depend upon any individual differences in appearance or personality. The child is loved for his own sake and the love is given without resentment of the demands placed upon the parent.

Table 3.8 9–12 months

Gross motor skills	Fine motor skills
The baby will now be mobile; she may be crawling, bear-walking, bottom-shuffling or even walking. She can sit up on her own and lean forwards to pick things up. She may crawl upstairs and onto low items of furniture. She may bounce in rhythm to music.	Her pincer grasp is now well developed and she can pick things up and pull them towards her She can poke with one finger and will point to desired objects. She can clap her hands and will imitate adult actions. She throws toys deliberately. She manages spoons and finger foods well.
Cognitive and language	**Emotional and social**
The baby may produce her first words – often 'dada', 'mama' or 'bye-bye'. She uses more expressive babbling now. She understands her daily routine and will follow simple instructions, e.g. kiss teddy.	The baby enjoys songs and action rhymes. She still likes to be near to a familiar adult. She can drink from a cup with help. She will play alone for long periods. She has and shows definite likes and dislikes at meals at at bedtimes.
THE ROLE OF THE CARER IN STIMULATING DEVELOPMENT	
Promoting physical development: Provide large-wheeled toys to push around – brick trucks serve the dual purpose of walking and stacking games. Ensure furniture is safe and stable for climbers. Swimming, walking in the park. Small climbing frames – closely supervised – to increase her balance and co-ordination. Stacking and nesting toys. Roll balls for her to bring back to you. Sand and water play – always supervised. Cardboard boxes and saucepans to put things into and take things out of.	**Promoting cognitive, emotional & social development:** Partake in plenty of talking to the baby which requires a response that will develop language ability. Encourage self-feeding; tolerate messes. Talk constantly to her and use rhymes and action songs. Offer lots of play opportunities with adult interaction – sharing, taking turns etc. Encourage her to join in and help with regular chores. Foster a feeling of self-worth by providing her with her own equipment and utensils – e.g. she will need her own flannel, toothbrush, cup and spoon.

Michael Rutter (1981) conducted a major review of maternal deprivation research and found – unlike Bowlby – that there is *not* a direct causal link between early experiences of separation from parents and later emotional distress. Rutter believed that:

> ▶ A distinction should be made between *disruption* of affectional bonds, (i.e. where there *has* been a bond established but that maternal care is lost) and between *privation* of affectional bonds, where children growing up in institutionalised care are denied the opportunity of establishing such bonds.

Table 3.9 12–15 months

Gross motor skills	Fine motor skills
The baby probably walks alone, with feet wide apart and arms raised to maintain balance. She is likely to fall over and sit down suddenly a lot. She can probably manage stairs and steps, but will need supervision. She can get to standing without help from furniture or people and kneels without support.	The baby can build with a few bricks and arrange toys on the floor. She holds crayon in palmar grasp. And turns several pages of a book at once. She can point to desired objects. The baby shows a preference for one hand but uses either.
Cognitive and language	**Emotional and social**
The baby learns new ways of solving problems. She uses trial and error methods to learn about objects. She speaks 2–6 or more recognizable words and demonstrates understanding of many more words.	The child is emotionally **labile**, that is, she is likely to have fluctuating moods. She is closely dependent upon adult's reassuring presence. She often wants a comfort object such as a teddy or a piece of cloth. She is still shy with strangers.
THE ROLE OF THE CARER IN STIMULATING DEVELOPMENT	
Promoting physical development: Provide stacking toys and bricks. Provide push-and-pull toys for children who are walking. Read picture books with simple rhymes. Big empty cardboard boxes are popular. Provide thick crayons or thick paint-brushes. Arrange a corner of the kitchen or garden for messy play involving the use of water or paint. **NB: This is high risk age for accidents – be vigilant at all times**	**Promting cognitive, emotional & social development:** Encourage creative activities such as painting or collage. Join in games of 'let's pretend' to develop the child's imagination. Think about attending a mother and toddler group or a one o'clock club (see page 000) Encourage role-play games of make-believe. Talk to her about everyday activities, but allow time for her to respond. Provide an interesting environment that contains pictures, music, books and food that stimulate the senses.

▶ A distinction should be made between the *disruption* of affectional bonds (e.g. if the mother has died) and the *distortion* of relationships within the family, brought about by separation or divorce (when the mother is still physically present).

Table 3.10 *Around 18 months*

Gross motor skills	Fine motor skills
The baby walks confidently and is able to stop without falling. She can kneel, squat, climb and carry things around with her. She can climb onto an adult chair forwards and then turn around to sit. She comes downstairs, usually by creeping backwards on her tummy.	The baby can pick up small objects using a delicate pincer grasp. She holds pencil mid-shaft or grasps near end and scribbles to and fro. She builds a tower of three or more cubes. She has good wrist control for manipulating objects. She can thread large beads.
Cognitive and language	**Emotional and social**
She knows the names of parts of her body, and can point to them on herself or on a doll when named. She is beginning to indulge in pretend and imitative play. She uses 6–20 recognisable words and understands many more. She repeats the last words of adult sentences. She indicates desires by pointing, urgent vocalisations or words. Obeys simple instructions e.g. 'shut the door', and where's pussy-cat'.	She develops a sense of identity. She has an increasing desire for independence. She enjoys being able to walk, and is eager to try to get dressed – 'me do it!' She has a longer memory; remembers where objects belong. Plays contentedly alone but likes to be near familiar adult or older sibling. Alternates between clinging and resistance. Personality traits becoming more evident. May indicate toilet needs by restlessless or vocalisation. Easily frustrated; occasional temper tantrums.
THE ROLE OF THE CARER IN STIMULATING DEVELOPMENT	
Promoting physical development: Provide walker trucks still, pull-along animals etc. Encourage play with messy materials: sand, water, play dough. Provide low, stable furniture to climb on. Provide pop-up toys, stacking toys and a peg or shape basher. Balls to kick or throw.	**Promoting cognitive, emotional & social development:** Provide toys which encourage make-believe play. Picture books of familiar objects and those that tell a simple story. Other people, other children – for conversation, finger-rhymes and singing. Models such as Duplo, dressing-up things to encourage fantasy play. Toy telephones and other pretend household objects to encourage language skills. Bath toys – simple beakers, sprinkling toys and waterproof books. **NB: Always supervise the child in the bath**

▶ The *quality* of family relationships affects the child more than the actual fact of separation or divorce; for example, children separated because of discord between their parents are more likely to show the sort of 'deprivation reaction' which Bowlby described than are children separated by the death of a parent.

▶ The separation of the child from the parents itself is not as significant as the quality of **sensitive support** given to the child during the experience of separation.

▶ **Multiple attachments** can be formed with various people without harm, as long as there is not an *extreme* form of shared care, e.g. with tens of adults involved.

▶ Children often appear to be extremely resilient to situations of deprivation; other factors – such as understimulation and minimal social contact – play an unquantifiable part in the overall picture of deprivation.

Bonding

It is now recognised that a bond of attachment is established over a period of time and that it is the *quality* of the time the child spends with people which determines whether or not the child becomes attached to them. Most mothers find that they establish a bond with their newborn babies within the first few days, but others find that it takes more time to develop.

THE ROLE OF THE FATHER

The strength of the attachment that children have to their fathers depends, (just as with any attachment), upon the *quality* of the relationship. Father and child will be securely attached when the father:

• is sensitive to the baby's signals;
• spends a lot of his time with the infant in face-to-face interaction;
• engages in play with the baby.

In general, infants prefer either the father or mother to a stranger, but when frightened or in distress babies are more likely to turn to the mother than to the father. Fathers have become more involved with their babies over the last two decades and many now attend the births of their babies to offer practical and emotional support to the mother.

The need to love every child is not an empty sentimental phrase. It means really caring that the child is suffering, even if you don't *like* him or her much. It also involves not hiding behind the psychology textbook words, such as attachment and bonding, but really listening to the meaning behind words.

2 The need for security

Children need a secure framework within which to develop. Above all, they need the security of stable family relationships. Children need to be able to rely on the reactions and behaviour of those around them in order to have the confidence to explore the wider world, for example, at nursery school or day nursery. They also need the security of a familiar place and known routine. Some children develop a need for what Winnicott called a **transitional object**. A transitional object may be a cuddly toy, a blanket or a piece of rag to which the baby becomes especially attached. It symbolises the union of the baby and mother at the time they are becoming separate in the baby's mind, and has been described as the 'first **not-me** possession'.

Figure 3.8   Baby with teddy

Such a familiar object gives a feeling of reassurance and security and is often needed at bedtime or in stressful situations. Very young children resist change. They prefer their world to be ordered and predictable. By allowing children to establish rituals and routines that are personal to them, parents and other caregivers acknowledge the child's right to freedom of expression and self-determination.

3 The need for new experiences

Children's learning depends upon their experiences. By presenting the baby with new experiences and allowing them to build upon previously learnt skills, the baby learns how to make sense of the world – in terms of using their physical abilities, as well as using their growing intellectual abilities and social awareness.

THE USE OF LANGUAGE

The development of language is closely allied to children's **intellectual and conceptual development**. It is an important milestone for the developing child as it enables higher levels of communication and a channel for expressing emotion and interacting with others. In rare instances where children have been deprived of language, emotional and social development becomes arrested.

4 The need for praise and recognition

Children need to have their achievements recognised and praised in order to persevere in their pursuit of knowledge about the world and the people around them. Encouragement and a reasonable level of expectation act as an incentive to perseverance. Children who are made to feel like failures when they do not live up to parents' unrealistic expectations become discouraged and make less effort. Children whose parents have too low expectations will similarly adopt a low level of effort and achievement.

5 The need for responsibility

This need is met by allowing children to gain personal independence. Babies delight in being able to develop skills such as feeding themselves and being able to get around without help. Later they are able to exercise freedom of taste in food, play, clothes, choice of friends and hobbies. Adults provide role models for children; what we actually do – or how we behave – influences childrens' behaviour far more than what we say.

Table 3.11   Factors influencing development

Diet	Drugs
Deficiencies and failure to thrive (see Chapter 5).	Taken by the mother during pregnancy, including tobacco and alcohol
Disease	**Genetic**
Chronic and severe acute infections	Including: ▶ Down's syndrome, cystic fibrosis ▶ sickle cell disease, sensory impairment

Physical
▶ effects of poor nutrition ▶ lack of sleep ▶ temporary or permanent hearing loss ▶ lack of opportunity for physical activity ▶ effects of physical disability or chronic illness

Emotional	Cultural and social
▶ lack of esteem and confidence ▶ effects of trauma/event e.g. bereavement, abuse, new baby etc.	▶ Different cultural expectations and experience ▶ poor role models ▶ limited social opportunities ▶ lack of a stable relationship with adults

Economic and environmental factors
▶ poor housing: contributing to increased accident rates, infections resulting from living in overcrowded conditions and poor nutrition ▶ water pollution: cause of amoebic dysentery, poliomyelitis virus, cholera and typhoid ▶ air pollution: a contributory cause of asthma and lead poisoning ▶ lack of stimulation, or too much stimulation ▶ poor provision for play

Factors influencing development

The interplay of various factors will influence the way a child grows and develops in all the developmental areas. One factor may affect another; for example, physical factors such as a hearing deficit may affect a child socially and emotionally and lead to lack of confidence and motivation. If a child lacks stimulation in his environment – in any area of development – he will miss out on important early learning activities which help in the development of concepts. Conditions such as Down's syndrome are usually, but not always, associated with learning difficulties. Language and comprehension may be very slow to develop and children will need lots of encouragement to communicate. Deafness has serious effects on both language and cognitive development, even when the condition is temporary, as in 'glue ear'.

Activities relating to Chapter 3

A C T I V I T Y   I

Promoting visual development (Solo or group activity)

Design a mobile

1   Think of two or more designs for the mobile. (You could use a coathanger or a cardboard tube as your basic structure.)
2   Compare the ideas, considering the following factors:

> ▶ availability of resources and materials;
> ▶ skills and time required;
> ▶ costs of materials;
> ▶ appropriateness of the design for its purpose;
> ▶ safety of the design.

3   Select one of the designs. If possible use a computer graphics program to prepare patterns and a word processor to write a set of instructions for making the mobile,
4   Follow your written instructions and make the mobile.
5   Evaluate both the instructions – were they easy to follow or did you have to modify the original plan? – and the mobile.
6   If possible, write a detailed observation of a baby reacting to the mobile for the first time.

A C T I V I T Y   2

Promoting sensory development

Design and make a simple game or toy that will encourage a baby's sensory development. Think about the stage of development the child has reached and plan to make a toy that will promote development of one or more of that baby's senses. Examples: Activity mat, sound lotto, 'feely' bag, matching smells.

Points to consider are:

- safety
- hygiene
- suitability for purpose

Try to describe the way in which the senses may be developed by using your game or toy and, if possible, write a detailed observation of the baby playing with it.

ACTIVITY 3

Promoting visual development in a baby aged 2–4 months

At around two months a baby will begin to follow movement with her eyes. One way of promoting visual development – and of improving head-eye co-ordination – in young babies is to:

1   Select a favourite toy – perhaps a teddy or a brightly coloured toy.
2   Hold the toy about one metre in front of her.
3   Slowly move the toy from side to side so that she can follow it with her eyes.
4   As she gets better at following the movement, swing the toy farther each way. Then try different directions, up and down, in and out.

ACTIVITY 4

Promoting the sense of touch: baby massage

Massage has many benefits for a baby. It is very soothing and can calm a fretful baby. It is also a very good way of showing love. The main points to remember are that the experience should:

> ► benefit both the baby and the carer, in calming the nerves and increasing the carers confidence in handling techniques;
> ► be conducted in a relaxed atmosphere, avoiding the distractions of telephone and other people;
> ► always be symmetrical, i.e. both sides of the baby's body should be massaged at the same time;
> ► take place in a warm room and be an unhurried, relaxing experience.

1   Work form the baby's head down, using a light circular motion. First massage the crown of the baby's head very gently, moving on to the forehead, cheeks and ears.

2   Gently massage her neck from her ears down to her shoulders, and from her chin to her chest.

3   Gently stroke her arms all the way to the fingertips, starting from the shoulders,

4   Stroke down the baby's chest and tummy, rubbing in a circular direction.

5   Gently massage her legs from the thighs to the ankles.

6   Massage her feet, stroking from heel to toe; concentrate on each toe individually.

7   Finally, turn her over onto her front and gently massage her back.

ACTIVITY 5

Object Permanence

Ask a willing parent of a baby aged between six and twelve months of age if you can try the Object Permanence activity with the baby:

1   Ask the parents for one of the baby's favourite playthings. Place the baby in a sitting position or on her stomach in such a way that she can reach for the toy easily.

2   While the baby is watching, place the toy in full view and within easy reach. Note if the baby reaches for the object.

3   Again, in full view of the baby, cover part of the toy with a cloth, so that only part of it is visible. Note if the baby reaches for the toy.

4   While the baby is reaching for the toy, cover it completely with the cloth. Note if the baby continues to reach for it.

5   While the baby is still interested in the toy, and again in full view of the baby, cover the whole toy with the cloth once more. Note if the baby tries to pull the cloth away or to search for the toy in some way.

Research shows that Step 3 – continuing to reach for the partly covered toy – is typically experienced at about 6 months; step 4 at about 7 months and Step 5 at about 8 months. Write up the results of your activity and compare with others.

ACTIVITY 6

Observing attachment

TASK ONE: NATURALISTIC OBSERVATION

Arrange to visit a home where there is a small child (aged between 3 months and 18 months). Explain that you want to observe the child's reaction to an unfamiliar situation as part of your study into children's emotional and social development.

Ask if you can pick up the child, play with her and be alone with her for a short while. Act in a friendly, natural way. Then record what happened as soon as possible afterwards:

- Did the child appear friendly or cautious?
- Did the child display a mixture of emotions? Try to build up an accurate picture of the child's emotions by describing facial expressions, vocalisations, gesture and body language.

Write an evaluation of the observation that includes your own personal learning about the nature of attachment and of mother-child separation.

TASK TWO: RESEARCH INTO ATTACHMENT IN CHILDHOOD

Different patterns of attachment or bonding occur in different parts of the world. Choose a different culture to research, e.g. Japanese society, the kibbutzim in Israel, China or Africa. Find out about the different child-rearing practices in the culture and relate this to the theories on attachment and personality.

ACTIVITY 7

Observing language development in adult-child interaction

Observe a one-to-one relationship between a mother and her young child under eighteen months. Choose an appropriate context such as bath-time, story-time or mealtime. Ask permission to make an audio tape of the language used and try to observe also the non-verbal communication used (See page 62).

After the activity:

- Make a transcript of the tape; do not use more than 5 minutes of the tape as transcripts take a long time to make.
- Analyse the transcript: write down the child's language and the mother's language, referring to the sections on Stages in Language Development and Baby Talk Register.
- Evaluate the language development of the child; note also the features of BTR used by the adult.

4

Physical Care of the Baby

Contents

Functions of the skin   Caring for a baby's skin   The role of bathing in holistic development   Bathing and 'topping and tailing' techniques   Care of skin and hair – including multi-cultural preferences   Care of the nappy area   Commonly encountered problems and disorders   Principles of dental care and oral health   Care of the feet   Establishing hygiene routines

Functions of the skin

A baby's skin is soft and delicate, yet forms a tough pliant covering for the body. The skin has many important functions:

- protection: it protects underlying organs and, when unbroken, protects against germs entering the body;
- secretion of oil (sebum): this lubricates the skin and gives hair its shine;
- excretion: the skin excretes waste products in sweat;
- sensation: each square inch of skin contains up to 1500 nerve endings called receptors which detect different feelings such as touch, cold, warmth, pressure, pain and hair movement;

- manufacture of vitamin D: vitamin D is made when skin is exposed to sunlight and is essential for healthy bones and teeth; black skin protects against sunburn but is less efficient at making vitamin D; black children may need a supplement of vitamin D in the winter;
- temperature regulation: the hypothalamus in the brain controls body temperature by releasing sweat, which evaporates from the skin's surface, cooling the body.

Caring for a baby's skin

A young baby does not have to be bathed every day because only her bottom, face and neck and skin creases get dirty. If a bath is not given daily, the baby should have the important body parts cleansed thoroughly – a process known as 'topping and tailing'. This process limits the amount of undressing and enables the newborn baby needs to be handled gently but firmly, and with confidence. Most babies learn to enjoy the sensation of water and are greatly affected by your attitude. The more relaxed and unhurried you are the more enjoyable will be the whole experience.

Topping and tailing

Babies do not like having their skin exposed to the air, so should be undressed for the shortest possible time. Always ensure the room is warm, not less than 20°C (68°F) and that there are not any draughts. Warm a large, soft towel on a not-too-hot radiator and have it ready to wrap the baby afterwards. Collect all the equipment you will need:

• Changing mat	• a small bowl of water that has been boiled and allowed to cool; this boiled water is important for a newborn baby, but from one month water may be used straight from the tap
• cotton wool swabs	• lidded buckets for soiled nappies, used swabs and clothes
• bowl of warm water	• a large soft towel
• clean clothes and a nappy	• protective cream e.g. vaseline

1 Wash your hands.
2 Remove the baby's clothes, leaving on her vest and nappy.
3 Wrap the baby in the towel, keeping her arms inside.
4 Clean the face: Use two separate pieces of cotton wool (one for each eye) squeezed in the boiled water and gently wipe the baby's eyes in one movement from the inner corner outwards (this will prevent any infection passing from one eye to the other)
5 Gently wipe all around the face and behind the ears. (Do not poke around inside her ears or nose; these areas are self-cleaning.) Lift her chin and wipe gently under the folds of skin. Dry each area thoroughly by patting with a soft towel or dry cotton wool.
6 Unwrap the towel and take the baby's vest off; raise each arm separately and wipe the armpit carefully as the folds of skin rub together here and can become quite sore – again dry thoroughly and dust with baby powder if used.
7 Until the cord has dropped off, make sure that it is kept clean and dry using special antiseptic powder supplied by the midwife.

8 Wipe and dry the baby's hands.
9 Take her nappy off and place in lidded bucket.
10 Clean her bottom with moist swabs, then wash with soap and water; rinse well with flannel or sponge, pat dry and apply protective cream.
11 Put on clean nappy and clothes.

Bathing the baby

When the bath is given will depend on family routines, but it is best not to bath the baby immediately after a feed, as she may be sick. Some babies love being bathed; others dislike even being undressed. Bathtime has several benefits for babies:

> ▶ the opportunity to kick and exercise;
> ▶ cleaning and refreshing the skin and hair;
> ▶ the opportunity for the carer to observe any skin problems – rashes, bruises etc.;
> ▶ a valuable time for communication between the baby and the carer;
> ▶ a time for relaxation and enjoyment.

As for 'topping and tailing', ensure the room is warm and draught-free and collect all necessary equipment:

- small bowl of boiled water and cotton swabs (as for 'topping and tailing' procedure)

- baby bath filled with warm water – test temperature with your elbow, (not with hands which are insensitive to high temperatures); the water should feel warm but not hot*

- changing mat
- 2 warmed towels
- brush and comb

- 2 lidded buckets
- clean nappy and clothes
- baby toiletries and nail scissors

Always fill any bath for a baby with cold water first, adding hot water until it feels just warm.

1 Undress the baby except for her nappy and wrap her in a towel whilst you clean her face; clean face as for 'topping and tailing'.
2 Wash her hair before putting her in the bath; support her head and neck with one hand, hold her over the bath and wash her head with plain water or baby shampoo; rinse head thoroughly and dry with second towel.
3 Unwrap towel; remove nappy and place in bucket.
4 Remove any soiling from the baby's bottom with cotton wool;

Figure 4.1   Baby being bathed

remember to clean baby girls from front to back to avoid germs from faeces entering the urethra or vagina.

5   Lay the baby in the crook of one arm and gently soap her body front and back with baby soap (If preferred, use baby bath liquid added to the bath beforehand.)

6   To place her in the bath, remove the towel and, supporting her shoulders with your forearm, hook your hand around her shoulder and under her armpit. Cradle her legs with your other hand and gently lower her into the water.

7   Talk to the baby and gently swish the water to rinse off the soap; pay particular attention to all skin creases – under arms, between legs and behind knees. Allow time for the baby to splash and kick but avoid chilling.

8   Lift the baby out and wrap in warm towel; dry her thoroughly by patting, not rubbing.

9   Baby oil or moisturiser may now be applied to the skin; do not use talcum powder *with* oils as it will form lumps and cause irritation.

10   Dress the baby in clean nappy and clothes.

Guidelines for bathing

- Cultural preferences in skin care should be observed; cocoa butter or special moisturisers are usually applied to babies with black skin and their bodies may be massaged with oil after bathing.
- Collect equipment and test temperature of water with your elbow or the inner side of your wrist; always put cold water in the bath before adding hot – many babies have been severely scalded by contact with the hot surface of the bath.
- Do not top up with hot water while the baby is in the bath; make sure that taps are turned off tightly as even small drops of hot water can cause scalds.
- Do not wear dangling earrings or sharp brooches and keep your own nails short and clean.
- **Never** leave a baby alone in the bath – even for a few seconds. A small baby can drown in a few inches of water.
- From a few months old, babies may be bathed in the big bath, keeping the water shallow and following the same guidelines regarding temperature and safety. A non-slip mat placed in the bottom of the bath will prevent slipping.
- Avoid talcum powder because of the risk of inhalation or allergy; if it is used, place on your hands first and then gently smooth it onto completely dry skin.
- Do not use cotton wool buds – they are not necessary and can be dangerous when poked inside a baby's ears or nose, which are self-cleansing anyway.
- Nail care should be included in the bathing routine. A young baby's nails should be cut when necessary after a bath when they are soft. Some parents use their own teeth to bite them gently off.
- Hair should be washed daily in the first few months, but shampoo is not necessary every day. A little bath lotion added to the bath water could be gradually worked into the baby's scalp until a lather forms and may then be rinsed off using a wrung out flannel.
- If the baby dislikes having her hair washed, try to keep hair washing separate from bath time so that the two are not associated as unpleasant events.

Nappies

The choice of nappies will depend on several factors: convenience, cost, personal preference and concern for the environment. There are two main types of nappy:

1 **Fabric nappies**: these are made from terry towelling and come in

different qualities and thickness. Two dozen are required for everyday use. Fabric nappies may be squares or shaped to fit. The latest style is similar in shape to the disposable nappy and has popper fastenings. If using fabric squares, you will also need special nappy safety pins, six pairs of plastic pants. Disposable one-way liners may be used with towelling nappies to keep wetness from the baby's skin and to make solid matter easier to dispose of down the toilet.

2 **Disposable nappies**: these are nappy, liner and plastic pants all in one and are available in a wide range of designs. Some have more padding at the front for boys and there are different absorbencies for day and night time use. Some makes have resealable tapes so that you can check if the nappy is clean.

Changing a nappy

Young babies will need several changes of nappy each day – whenever the nappy is wet or soiled. As with any regular routine, have everything ready before you begin:

- a plastic-covered padded changing mat
- a bowl of warm water (or baby wipes)
- baby lotion
- barrier cream e.g. zinc and castor oil

- nappy sacks for dirty nappies
- cotton wool
- baby bath liquid
- new, clean nappy

If you are using a special changing table or bed, make sure the baby cannot fall off. Never leave the baby unattended on a high surface. As long as there are no draughts and the room is warm, the changing mat can be placed on the floor.

Cleaning a girl

1 First wash your hands and put the baby girl on the changing mat.
2 Undo her clothing and open out the nappy.
3 Clean off as much faeces as possible with the soiled nappy.
4 Use wet cotton wool or baby wipes to clean inside all the skin creases at the top of her legs. Wipe down towards her bottom.
5 Lift her legs using one hand (finger between her ankles) and clean her buttocks and thighs with fresh cotton wool, working inwards towards the anus. Keep clear of her vagina and never clean inside the lips of the vulva.
6 Dry the skin creases and the rest of the nappy area thoroughly. Let her kick freely and then apply barrier cream.

Cleaning a boy

1 First wash your hands and place the baby boy on the changing mat. It is quite common for baby boys to urinate just as you remove the nappy, so pause for a few seconds with the nappy held over the penis.
2 Moisten cotton wool with water or lotion and begin by wiping his tummy across, starting at his navel.
3 Using fresh cotton wool or a wipe, clean the creases at the top of his legs working down towards his anus and back.
4 Wipe all over the testicles holding his penis out of the way. Clean under the penis. Never try to pull back the foreskin.
5 Lift his legs using one hand (finger between his ankles) and wipe away from his anus, to buttocks and to back of thighs.
6 Dry the skin creases and the rest of the nappy area thoroughly. Let him kick freely and then apply barrier cream.

Methods of folding fabric nappies

There are two main ways of folding fabric nappies:

- **the triple absorbent fold**: this is the most suitable method for a newborn baby and is a neat shape. It is unsuitable for larger babies.

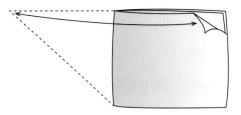

a) Lift the top layer of the nappy by the right-hand corner

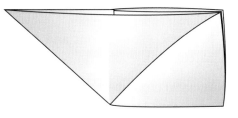

b) Pull the corner to the left to make a triangle

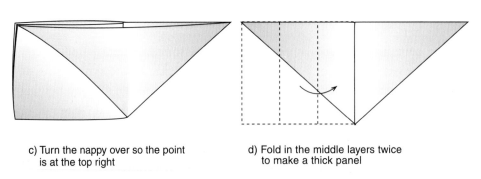

c) Turn the nappy over so the point is at the top right

d) Fold in the middle layers twice to make a thick panel

Figure 4.2a, b, c, d. Triple absorbent fold

Start with a square nappy folded into four to make a smaller square with the open edges to the top and to the right.
- **the kite fold**: this is suitable for a larger baby and the depth of the kite can be adjusted to suit the size of the baby.

NAPPY RASH

Almost all babies have occasional bouts of redness and soreness in the area of their nappies; it may be caused by leaving wet and dirty nappies on too long, poor washing techniques, infections, skin disorders such as **eczema** or **seborrhoeic dermatitis** or reaction to creams or detergents.

The most common types of nappy rash are:

- candidiasis or thrush dermatitis
- ammonia dermatitis

Thrush dermatitis

This is caused by an organism *candida albicans*, a yeast fungus that lives naturally in many parts of the body. The rash is pink and pimply and is seen in the folds of the groin and around the anus and genital area; it is sometimes caused in breastfed babies whose mothers have taken a course of antibiotics, or in bottlefed babies where the teats have been inadequately cleaned and sterilised.

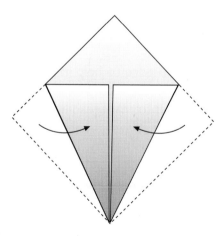

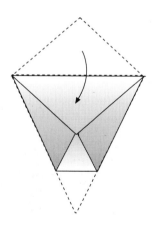

a) Fold the sides in to the centre to make a kite shape

b) Fold the point at the top down to the centre. Fold the bottom point up to fit the size of the baby.

Figure 4.3a, b.   Kite fold

TREATMENT

- Use a special anti-fungal cream prescribed by the doctor at each nappy change.
- Do not use zinc and castor oil cream until clear of infection as the thrush organism thrives on it.
- If oral thrush is present a prescribed ointment may be used.

AMMONIA DERMATITIS

This produces the most severe type of nappy rash and is caused by the ammonia present in the baby's urine and stools reacting with the baby's skin. It is more common in bottlefed babies because their stools are more alkaline and provide a better medium for the organisms to thrive. The rash is bright red, may be ulcerated and covers the genital area; the ammonia smells very strongly and causes the baby a lot of burning pain.

TREATMENT

- Wash with mild soap and water and dry gently.
- Expose the baby's bottom to fresh air as much as possible.
- Only use creams if advised and leave plastic pants off;
- If using towelling nappies, a solution of 30 ml vinegar to 2 litres of warm water should be used as a final rinsing solution to neutralise the ammonia.

CARE OF THE TEETH

Although not yet visible, the teeth of a newborn baby are already developing inside the gums. A baby's first teeth are called primary teeth or milk teeth and start to appear at around six months (see Figure 4.5).

There are 20 primary teeth in all and they are of three types:

- **incisors**: tough, chisel-shaped teeth with a sharp edge to help in biting food;
- **canines**: pointed teeth which help to tear food into manageable chunks;
- **molars**: large, strong teeth that grind against each other to crush food.

Rarely, a baby is born with the first tooth and it may have to be removed, if loose. Most children have 'cut' all twenty primary teeth by the age of 3 years; the two front teeth on the lower jaw are usually the first, followed by those on the upper jaw.

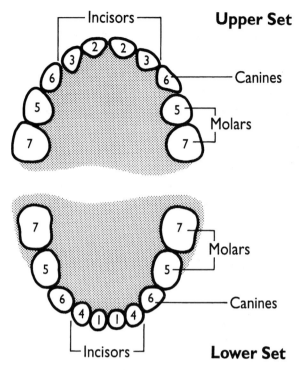

Figure 4.4   The usual order in which primary teeth appear

Teething

Some babies cut their teeth with no ill effects; others may experience:

- general fretfulness and rubbing mouth or ears;
- red or sore patches around the mouth;
- diarrhoea;
- a bright red flush on one or both cheeks and on the chin;
- dribbling.

Teething should not be treated as an illness, but babies will need comforting if in pain. Teething rings and hard rusks usually provide relief, but teething powders and gels are not advised, as they are dangerous if given in large quantities. Infant paracetamol may be helpful in relieving pain but is unsuitable for babies under three months unless advised by the doctor.

Caring for teeth

Teeth need cleaning as soon as they appear, because **plaque** sticks to the teeth and will cause decay if not removed. Caring for the temporary first teeth is important because:

- it develops a good hygiene habit which will continue throughout life;

- if milk teeth decay, they may need to be extracted; this could lead to crowding in the mouth as the natural gaps for the second teeth to fill will be too small;
- painful teeth may prevent chewing and cause eating problems;
- clean, white shining teeth look good.

Healthy teeth require:

- a healthy well-balanced diet by the mother during pregnancy, especially foods rich in protein, calcium and vitamin D;
- avoidance of sugary foods, drinks and medicines;
- fluoride (see below);
- routine care of teeth; the baby should have her own toothbrush, kept clean and separate from others.

Cleaning a baby's teeth

Use a small amount of baby toothpaste on a soft baby toothbrush or a piece of fine cloth (e.g. muslin) to clean the plaque from the teeth. Gently smooth the paste on to her teeth and rub lightly. Rinse the brush in clear water and clean her mouth. Brush twice a day – after breakfast and before bed. After the first birthday, children can be taught to brush their own teeth – but will need careful supervision. They should be shown when and how to brush, that is, up and down away from the gum; they may need help to clean the back molars.

FLUORIDE

Some toothpastes contain fluoride, which is a mineral that can help prevent dental decay. Some water boards in the UK add fluoride to the water supply; in areas where the fluoride level is low, dentists recommend giving fluoride drops daily to children from six months of age until teething is complete (usually by age 12). If water in your area has added fluoride, do not give drops or tablet supplements as an excess of the mineral can cause mottling of the teeth.

DIET

Healthy teeth need calcium, fluoride, vitamins A, C and D, and foods that need chewing, such as apples, carrots and wholemeal bread. Sugar causes decay and can damage teeth even before they have come through. 'Dinky feeders' and baby bottles filled with sweet drinks are very harmful, because the teeth are kept bathed in sugar for a long time. It is better to save sweets and sugary snacks for special occasions only, or at least after meals, and to clean teeth thoroughly afterwards.

VISITING THE DENTIST

The earlier a child is introduced to the family dentist, the less likely she is to feel nervous about dental inspection and treatment. Try to arrange for her to accompany a parent or carer when they visit the dentist. NHS dental treatment is free for children and for women during pregnancy and during her child's first year. Once the child is about two, she should visit the dentist regularly to make sure her teeth are healthy and growing properly.

Care of the feet

- Feet should always be dried thoroughly between the toes and clean socks put on every day.
- All-in-one baby suits must be large enough not to cramp the baby's growing feet.
- Toenails should be cut straight across, not down into the corners.

Establishing hygiene routines

Having routines for everyday activities is reassuring for both babies and their carers and also ensures that care is consistent and of a high quality. This does not mean that caring for babies is, or should be, in itself a routine activity. Anyone looking after a baby needs to be able to adapt to her individual needs which will change from day to day. Therefore some flexibility is also desirable.

Activities relating to Chapter 4

ACTIVITY I

Bathing and topping and tailing

Prepare two illustrated posters or leaflets which describes:

> ▶ A topping and tailing routine for a newborn baby;
> ▶ A bath-time routine for a baby aged 3–6 months.

Try to implement these routines in practical placement and evaluate them.

A C T I V I T Y   2

Which nappies?

Research the advantages and disadvantages of fabric nappies and disposable nappies, including the following information:

> ▶ costs – initial outlay and on-going costs of laundry and purchase of nappies, liners, pants etc.;
> ▶ the effects of each method on the environment – chemicals used in laundering; disposal;
> ▶ convenience and suitability for the purpose;
> ▶ availability and costs of visiting laundry service for fabric nappies in your area.

A C T I V I T Y   3

A dental hygiene routine

Prepare a leaflet for parents showing how teeth develop in a young baby and how to ensure their healthy development. Include tips for making caring for the teeth an enjoyable routine activity.

5

Feeding the Baby

Contents

Nutritional needs of babies   Breastfeeding and bottlefeeding   Principles and routines   Preparation and storage of bottles and solid foods   Weaning and suggested diet   Equipment for feeding   Problems associated with feeding, e.g. allergies, colic, food intolerance, pyloric stenosis   Elimination and associated problems   Toilet training   Safety, hygiene and where to obtain advice

Nutritional needs of babies

The way babies and children are fed is much more than simply providing enough food to meet nutritional requirements; for the newborn baby, sucking milk is a great source of pleasure and is also rewarding and enjoyable for the mother. The ideal food for babies to start life with is breast milk and breastfeeding should always be encouraged as the first choice in infant feeding; however mothers should not be made to feel guilty or inadequate if they choose not to breastfeed their babies.

Advantages of breastfeeding

> ▶ Human milk provides food constituents in the correct balance for human growth. There is no trial and error to find the right formula to suit the baby.
> ▶ The milk is sterile and at the correct temperature; there is no need for bottles and sterilising equipment.
> ▶ Breast milk initially provides the infant with maternal antibodies and helps protect the child from infection.
> ▶ The child is less likely to become overweight as overfeeding by concentrating the formula is not possible, and the infant has more freedom of choice as to how much milk she will suckle.

> ▶ Generally breast milk is considered cheaper despite the extra calorific requirement of the mother.
> ▶ Sometimes it is easier to promote the mother-infant bonding by breastfeeding, although this is certainly not always the case.
> ▶ Some babies have an intolerance to the protein in cows' milk.
> ▶ The uterus returns to its pre-pregnancy state more quickly, by action of oxytocin released when the baby suckles.

The advantages of bottlefeeding

> ▶ The mother knows exactly how much milk the baby has taken.
> ▶ The milk is in no way affected by the mother's state of health, whereas anxiety, tiredness, illness or menstruation may reduce the quantity of breast milk.
> ▶ The infant is unaffected by such factors as maternal medication. Laxatives, antibiotics, alcohol and drugs affecting the central nervous system can affect the quality of breast milk.
> ▶ Other members of the family can feed the infant. In this way the father can feel equally involved with the child's care, and during the night could take over one of the feeds so that the mother can get more sleep.
> ▶ There is no fear of embarrassment while feeding.
> ▶ The mother is physically unaffected by feeding the infant, avoiding such problems as sore nipples.

Breastfeeding

The breast is made up of fifteen to twenty segments or lobes; each lobe contains alveoli, cells that produce milk. Lactiferous ducts drain milk from the alveoli to reservoirs in the area of the areola (the pigmented ring around the nipple). Small glands in the areola called Montgomery's tubercles produce a fluid that keeps the skin of the nipples and the areola soft and supple.

The nipple has several openings through which the baby can obtain milk. During pregnancy the breasts produce colostrum, a creamy yellowish fluid, low in fat and sugar, which is uniquely designed to feed the newborn baby. Colostrum also has higher levels of antibodies than mature milk and plays an important part in protecting the baby from infection. Mature milk is present

Figure 5.1   Father bottlefeeding

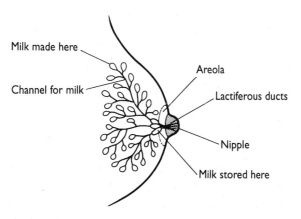

Figure 5.2   The lactating breast

in the breasts around the third day after birth. Hormonal changes in the mother's bloodstream cause the milk to be produced and the sucking of the baby stimulates a steady supply. (Unfortunately, this mechanism also operates in the event of stillbirth or miscarriage and can cause the mother severe distress, especially if she has had no warning.)

Management of breastfeeding

The most difficult part of breastfeeding is usually the beginning and it may take two to three weeks to establish a supply and to settle into some sort of pattern. Even if the mother does not intend to breastfeed her baby, she is encouraged to try for the first few days so that the baby can benefit from the unique properties of **colostrum**. Many of the problems that cause women to give up breastfeeding could be overcome with the right advice and support. Successful management of breastfeeding involves:

- the mother taking a well-balanced diet; her diet will affect the composition of the breast milk and some foods may cause colic. (Vegetarian mothers who drink cow's milk, eat a varied vegetarian diet and take vitamin supplements produce breast milk similar in nutrient value to non-vegetarian mothers; vegan mothers may need to take calcium and vitamin B12 supplements while breastfeeding);
- putting the baby to the breast straight after the birth. This has been shown to be a key factor in successful breastfeeding;
- feeding on demand – i.e. when the baby is hungry, rather than routinely every four hours.
- extra help in the home if possible, at least until breastfeeding is established;
- finding the most comfortable position for feeding; if the mother has a sore perineum or Caesarean scar, the midwife or health visitor will be able to advise;
- not giving extra (complementary) feeds by bottle;
- letting the baby decide when she has had enough milk and allowing her to finish sucking at one breast before offering the other.

Breast milk may be expressed by hand or by breast pump for use when the mother is unavailable; EBM or expressed breast milk can be stored in a sterilised container in a freezer for up to 3 months.

Bottlefeeding

Cow's milk is the ideal food for calves but is not suitable for babies as it contains three times as much protein, which is difficult to digest. as breast milk. Commercially modified baby milks (formula milks) must be used for bottlefeeding. Soya-based milks can be used if the baby develops an intolerance to modified cow's milks. For the first four to six months the baby will be given infant milk (formula) as a substitute for breast milk; she may then progress on to follow-on milk which should be offered until the age of 12 months.

Preparation of feeds

A day's supply of bottles may be made and stored in the fridge for up to 24 hours. A rough guide to quantities is: 150 ml of milk per kilogram of body weight per day; thus a baby weighing 4 kg will require approximately 600 ml in 24 hours. This could be given as 6 × 100 ml bottles.

The following equipment will be needed:

- a container for sterilising bottles, large enough to submerge everything completely; steam sterilisers are very effective but costly;
- eight wide-necked feeding bottles and teats designed for newborn babies;
- large plastic or Pyrex measuring jug and a plastic stirrer – or feeds can be made directly in the bottles and shaken to mix;
- sterilising liquid or tablets – check manufacturer's instructions for length of time and correct dilution.

It is very important that all bottles and equipment are thoroughly sterilised

- After use, scrub all the bottles, caps and covers, using hot soapy water and a special bottlebrush. Rinse thoroughly in clean running water.
- Teats may be cleaned using a special teat cleaner; turn teat inside out to ensure all milk deposits are removed and wash as the bottles.
- Submerge bottles, teats and all other equipment needed for bottlefeeding in the sterilising solution, checking that no bubbles are trapped inside bottles and that teats are completely immersed.

Guidelines to bottlefeeding

- Always wash hands thoroughly when preparing feeds for babies.
- Never add sugar or salt to the milk, and never make the feed stronger than the instructions state – this could result in too high a salt intake that can lead to severe illness.
- Always check the temperature of the milk before giving it to a baby.

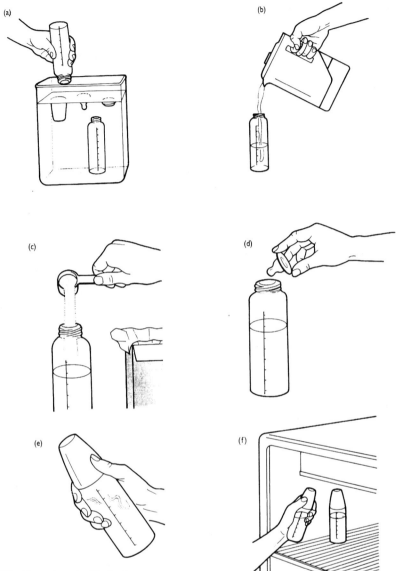

Figure 5.3   Preparing a bottle feed

- Try a few drops on your wrist; it should feel neither neither hot nor cold to the touch.
- Do not use a microwave oven to warm the bottle as it may produce isolated hot spots. Expressed breast milk should not be microwaved because it breaks down the natural chemistry.
- Always allow bottles to cool before placing in fridge.
- Always check that the teat has a hole the right size and that it is not blocked.
- Never prop up a baby with a bottle – choking is a real danger.
- Always supervise siblings when feeding small babies.

Giving a bottlefeed

1 Collect all the necessary equipment before picking up the baby; the bottle may be warmed in a jug of hot water or in a bottle warmer; have muslin square/bib and tissues to hand.
2 Check the temperature and flow of the milk by dripping it onto the inside of your wrist (it should feel warm, not hot or cold).
3 Make yourself comfortable with the baby; do not rush the feed – babies always sense if you are not relaxed and it can make them edgy too.
4 Try to hold the baby in a similar position to that for breastfeeding and maintain eye contact; this is a time for cuddling and talking to the baby.
5 Stimulate the rooting reflex (see page 33) by placing the teat at the corner of the baby's mouth; then put the teat fully into her mouth and feed by tilting the bottle so that the hole in the teat is always covered with milk.
6 After about 10 minutes, the baby may need to be helped to bring up wind; this can be done by leaning her forwards on your lap and gently rubbing her back or by holding her against your shoulder. Unless the baby is showing discomfort, do not insist on trying to produce a 'burp' – the baby may pass it out in the nappy.
7 If the baby dozes off during a feed, she may have wind that is making her feel full. Sit her more upright and gently rub her back for a couple of minutes. Then offer her more milk. Remember to angle the bottle so that the teat is full of milk, with no air spaces.
8 When the baby has finished her feed, pull the bottle firmly away. If she still wants to suck, offer her your clean little finger. Release suction when a baby will not let go of the bottle by sliding your little finger between her gums and the teat.

When breastfeeding is not possible

Some women are unable to breastfeed; this may be because:

- **they are seriously ill;**
- **they have to take certain drugs;**
- **they have a baby with a physical or mental disability.**

There is also a larger group of women who begin breastfeeding and give up because they run into problems. These problems include:

- **recurrent bouts of sore, cracked nipples, infective mastitis or breast abscesses;**
- **babies who fail to gain weight.**

Some women feel very strongly that they do not want to try breastfeeding. In fact, only a minority of babies are breastfed for more than a week or so after birth, and only a tiny minority are given nothing at all except breast milk for several months. Manufacturers of formula milks spend millions of pounds a year advertising baby milks and feeding equipment. The names of formula milks are so well known to all mothers that bottlefeeding may seem the best option. Many mothers are desperately disappointed when they have to switch from breast to bottlefeeding and these mothers need a lot of support and understanding.

Choice of equipment for feeding

Breastfeeding is sometimes difficult to get established, particularly for first time mothers. If the mother is returning to work, she may decide to express her breast milk for the nanny or nursery staff to give to her baby. Some mothers manage to express their milk manually; others will use either a manual or an electric breast pump. Both methods will involve the use of a strerilised collecting bottle and a sterile teat.

Sterilising equipment

Before starting to prepare feeds, it is vital that the equipment used is thoroughly washed with hot water and detergent, rinsed and then sterilised. Babies are very susceptible to germs and milk is an ideal breeding ground for bacteria. Use a bottle brush to ensure the insides of the bottles are clean and then squirt soapy water through the teats. It is also important to wash the locking rings, caps and bottle tops too. There are three different methods of sterilising the baby's feeding equipment:

- steam sterilising;
- microwave steam sterilising;
- cold water chemical sterilising.

Boiling is an alternative method of sterilisation, but teats that have been frequently boiled will need regular replacement, as they become sticky.

BOTTLES AND TEATS

Most bottles today are made of clear plastic and are designed to be unbreakable. However, they can develop cracks with sharp edges so should be checked every time that they are washed. Disposable bottle systems require the use of a fresh plastic liner at every feed. Teats are made from latex or silicone. The rubber teats last on average two to three months and should be discarded when they show signs of deterioration. Silicone teats tend to last up to a year.

DUMMIES

Babies are born with a strong sucking reflex and some babies are more 'sucky' than others are. If a dummy is used before the baby is weaned, it should be sterilised in the same way as teats are sterilised. For older babies careful washing and rinsing is sufficient. To prevent accidental strangulation, never hang a dummy from a ribbon or string around the baby's neck, nor from a cot rail.

Feeding problems in babies

Possetting

The baby regularly vomits small amounts of her feed but is generally healthy and has no signs of illness. It is caused by a weakness of the muscle at the opening of the stomach and eventually – usually by 6 to 8 months – the baby will grow out of it; although messy, there is no cause for alarm! It may be helped by sitting the baby upright in a rigid baby chair for half an hour after feeding.

Pyloric stenosis

This is a condition, commoner in boys than in girls, where the muscle surrounding the channel at the end of the stomach (the pylorus) thickens, narrowing the outlet. Symptoms usually appear about three weeks after birth:

- the baby will vomit – called **projectile vomiting,** as it often shoots several feet away;
- the baby becomes constipated;
- dehydration may occur and weight gain stops.

Medical advice should be sought; pyloric stenosis is easily diagnosed and usually cured by a simple operation.

Colic

Colic is an attack of abdominal pain caused by spasms in the intestines as food is being digested; sometimes called 'three month colic' as it usually disappears by 3 months, colic causes the baby to draw up her arms and legs and to cry inconsolably. Attacks of colic can last anything from a quarter of an hour to several hours and some babies only suffer in the evening. There is no known cause and no really effective cure; the obvious distress of the baby and the helplessness of the carer makes caring for a colicky baby difficult.

Parents need a lot of support and reassurance that the baby will grow out of it and that there is no lasting damage.

Alternative therapies include **chiropractic**. A practitioner of chiropractic may practise manipulation of the baby's spine, usually massaging the baby's spine, head, neck and hips. Little research has been done to assess the success of such methods and unfortunately it is a costly therapy.

Vomiting

When large amounts of breast milk or formula milk are regurgitated and if the baby is **failing to thrive**, a feed thickener (e.g. Gaviscon by Reckitt & Colman or Carobel by Cow & Gate) is recommended. These thickeners contain an antacid and should be given immediately before a feed. They are only available on prescription.

Food intolerance

Only a small number of reactions to food are true allergic responses, in that they involve an immune reaction in the body. Some babies develop an intolerance to cow's milk protein; the most common symptoms are vomiting, diarrhoea and **failure to thrive**. After weaning, foods most likely to cause an adverse reaction in babies are:

- hen's eggs
- wheat and other cereals
- fish
- pork
- citrus fruits

Allergies to food additives, such as the colouring agent **tartrazine**, have been blamed for many different problems, including eczema, asthma and hyperactivity (**Attention Deficit Disorder**); however, there is no conclusive medical evidence to support this thesis. Sometimes an allergic reaction will be temporary, perhaps following an illness, but the offending food should always be removed from the baby's diet. Dietetic advice should be sought before any changes to a balanced diet are made.

Weaning

Weaning is the gradual introduction of solid food to the baby's diet. The reasons for weaning are:

1 To meet the baby's nutritional needs – from about six months of age, milk alone will not satisfy the baby's increased nutritional requirements, especially for iron.

2 To develop the chewing mechanism; the muscular movement of the
    mouth and jaw also aids the development of speech.
3 To satisfy increasing appetite.
4 To introduce new tastes and textures; this enables the baby to join in
    family meals, thus promoting cognitive and social development.
5 To develop new skills – use of feeding beaker, cup and cutlery.

Stages of weaning

Between three and six months is usually the right time to start feeding solids
to a baby; giving solids too early – often in the mistaken belief that the baby
might sleep through the night – places a strain on the baby's immature
digestive system. It may also make her fat and increases the likelihood of
allergy.

STAGE 1 (FROM 3–6 MONTHS)

Pureed vegetables, pureed fruit, baby rice, finely pureed dahl or lentils.

Milk continues to be the most important food.

STAGE 2 (ABOUT 6–8 MONTHS)

Increase variety; introduce pureed or minced meat, chicken, liver, fish,
lentils, and beans. Raw eggs should not be used (see page 000) but cooked
egg yolk can be introduced from 6 months; wheat-based foods e.g. mashed
Weetabix, pieces of bread. Milk feeds decrease as more solids rich in protein
are offered

STAGE 3 (ABOUT 9–12 MONTHS)

Cow's milk can safely be used at about 12 months; lumpier foods such as
pasta, pieces of cooked meat, soft cooked beans, pieces of cheese, a variety
of breads; additional fluids such as diluted unsweetened fruit juice or water.
Three regular meals should be taken as well as drinks.

Methods of weaning

Some babies take very quickly to solid food; others appear not to be
interested at all. The baby's demands are a good guide for weaning; meal
times should never become a battleground. Even babies as young as four
months have definite food preferences and should never be forced to eat a
particular food, however much thought and effort has gone into the
preparation. Table 5.1 gives guidelines on introducing new solids to babies.
The best foods to start with are pureed cooked vegetables, fruit, and ground

cereals such as rice. Chewing usually starts at around the age of six months – whether the baby has teeth or not – and coarser textures can then be offered. The baby should be in a bouncing cradle or high chair – not in the usual feeding position in the carer's arms.

Methods of pureeing food

- rub through a sieve using a large spoon;
- mash soft foods such as banana or cooked potato with a fork;
- use a mouli-sieve or hand-blender;
- an electric blender (useful for larger amounts).

Guidelines for weaning

From 3–6 months, the first foods offered should:

✓ have a smooth consistency;
✓ be gluten-free;
✓ have a bland taste;
✓ not have salt or sugar added to them.

From 6–9 months, introduce:

✓ foods with stronger flavours and different textures;
✓ a wider range of wheat based foods, such as bread and breakfast cereals;
✓ small amounts of fish and a wider range of meats;
✓ finger foods. Start with soft foods such as cheese, banana, bread, and then try harder foods such as rusks and toast.

NB: Always stay while the baby is feeding, in case of choking

✓ small amounts of cow's milk to mix with solid food;
✓ a wider range of dairy products.

In general:

- try to encourage a liking for savoury foods;
- only introduce one new food at a time;
- be patient if the baby does not take the food – feed at the baby's pace, not yours;
- let the baby try lots of different foods;
- make sure that food is the right temperature;
- avoid giving sweet foods or drinks between meals;
- never leave a baby when she is eating;
- limit the use of commercially prepared foods – they are of poorer

Table 5.1 Introducing new solids to babies

	4–6 months	6–8 months	9–12 months
You can give or add	Puréed fruit Puréed vegetables Thin porridge made from oat or rice flakes or cornmeal Finely puréed dhal or lentils	A wider range of puréed fruits and vegetables Purées which include chicken, fish and liver Wheat-based foods, e.g. mashed Weetabix Egg yolk, well cooked Small-sized beans such as aduki beans, cooked soft Pieces of ripe banana Cooked rice Citrus fruits Soft summer fruits Pieces of bread	An increasingly wide range of foods with a variety of textures and flavours Cows' milk Pieces of cheese Fromage frais or yoghurt Pieces of fish Soft cooked beans Pasta A variety of breads Pieces of meat from a casserole Well-cooked egg white Almost anything that is wholesome and that the child can swallow.
How	Offer the food on the tip of a clean finger or on the tip of a clean (plastic or horn) teaspoon	On a teaspoon	On a spoon or as finger food
When	A very tiny amount at first, during or after a milk feed	At the end of a milk feed	At established meal times
Why	The start of transition from milk to solids	To introduce other foods when the child is hungry	To encourage full independence
Not yet	Cows' milk – or any except breast or formula milk Citrus fruit Soft summer fruits Wheat (cereals, flour, bread etc.) Spices Spinach, swede, turnip, beetroot Eggs Nuts Salt Sugar Fatty food	Cows' milk, except in small quantities mixed with other food Chillies or chilli powder Egg whites Nuts Salt Sugar Fatty food	Whole nuts Salt Sugar Fatty food

quality and will not allow the baby to become used to home cooking.
• select foods approved by the baby's parents.

Excretion

1 Bowel function

In the digestive process, food passes through the stomach into the small intestine and from there into the large intestine. Its waste products are stored in the rectum and then finally eliminated from the body as faeces. A baby cannot control, even for a second, the reflex that causes the rectum to empty. This gastrocolic reflex stimulates the rectum to empty every time that food enters the stomach; this is why young babies usually have a bowel movement with each feed

The first 'stool' or motion a newborn baby passes is **meconium** – a greenish-black treacle-like substance that is present in the baby's bowels before birth and is usually passed within 48 hours of birth. Once the baby starts to feed on milk, the stools change:

• a breastfed baby has fluid, yellow mustard-coloured stools which do not smell unpleasant;
• a bottlefed baby has more formed stools which are browner and may smell slightly;

Bottlefed babies tend to pass stools more often than breastfed babies, possibly because there is little waste. As the baby is weaned onto solid foods and starts to eat a more varied diet, her stools will alter in colour and consistency. Each child develops their own pattern of bowel movements; some may have a movement once or twice a day, or every two days.

CHANGES IN BOWEL MOVEMENTS

It is quite normal for a baby's stools to look different from one day to the next. If the baby is being breastfed any food eaten by the mother will affect the baby and may show a difference in the stools.

CONSTIPATION

Constipation means that there are long or irregular intervals between bowel movements. When a motion is passed, it is accompanied by pain and abdominal discomfort and the stools are hard and dry. In babies, these may look like little marbles. (Some babies will grunt and go red when they pass a motion – this is normal.) Constipation is more common in bottlefed babies than in breastfed babies

NB: If the baby is severely constipated, or passes blood in her stools, seek medical advice.

- A young baby may be given extra boiled water between feeds.
- Older babies should be given plenty of fluids and more fibre-rich foods such as fruit and vegetables, wholemeal bread and cereals in their diet.
- Do not give a laxative without first consulting a doctor.
- Do not add sugar to the baby's bottle.

BLOOD IN THE STOOLS

This should always be taken seriously, although the cause may be minor, for example, a small crack in the skin around the anus. Seek medical advice in case the presence of blood is an indication of an intestinal infection.

DIARRHOEA

Diarrhoea is caused by food passing through the intestines too quickly, not leaving enough time for it to be digested; the baby will pass frequent, loose watery stools. They may look greenish and smell different from the baby's usual stools. It should always be taken seriously in a young baby, especially if accompanied by vomiting, as there is the risk of **dehydration**. Seek medical advice and

- give cooled, boiled water only;
- bottle feeding of formula milk should be stopped, but breastfeeding may continue if the baby wants it.

If the baby is dehydrated the fontanelles will be sunken and she may be fretful and refusing feeds.

2 Bladder function

Once food has been absorbed into the bloodstream, waste is removed from the blood by the kidneys and eliminated from the body as urine. A young baby's bladder will empty itself automatically and frequently; as soon as it contains a little urine, the bladder wall stretches and the emptying action is stimulated. As she grows the baby's bladder will become capable of holding more urine for longer periods of time.

If the baby's urine is strong and concentrated, this is an indication of dehydration. If the urine remains strong after giving extra fluids, or if the smell is offensive, there may be a urinary infection. Seek medical advice.

THE DEVELOPMENT OF BOWEL AND BLADDER CONTROL

Newborn babies pass the waste products of digestion automatically; in other words, although they may go red in the face when passing a stool or motion, they have no conscious control over the action. Parents used to boast with pride that all their children were potty trained at nine months, but the reality is that they were just lucky in their timing! Up to the age of about 18 months, emptying of the bladder and bowel is still a totally automatic reaction – the child's central nervous system (CNS) is still not sufficiently mature to make the connection between the action and its results.

Toilet training

There is no point in attempting to start toilet training until the toddler shows that he or she is ready, and this rarely occurs before the age of 18 months. The usual signs are:

*   increased interest when passing urine or a motion; she may pretend play on the potty with her toys;
*   she may tell the carer when she has passed urine or a bowel motion or look very uncomfortable;
*   she may start to be more regular with bowel motions or the wet nappies may become rarer.

Toilet training should be approached in a relaxed, unhurried manner. If the potty is introduced too early, or if a child is forced to sit on it for long periods of time, she may rebel and the whole issue of toilet training becomes a battleground.

Toilet training can be over in a few days or may take some months. Becoming dry at night takes longer, but most children manage this before the age of 5.

Guidelines for toilet training

✓ Before attempting to toilet train a child, make sure she has shown that she is *ready* to be trained, and remember that there is, as with all other developmental milestones, a wide variation in the age range at which children achieve bowel and bladder control.

✓ Be relaxed about toilet training and be prepared for accidents.

✓ Have the potty in the home so that the child becomes familiar with it and can include it in her play.

✓ Some children feel insecure when sitting on a potty with no nappy on – try it first with nappy or pants on if she shows reluctance.

✓ It is easier to attempt toilet training in fine weather when the child can run around without nappies or pants on.

✓ It helps if the child sees other children using the toilet or potty.

✓ If you start training when there is a new baby expected, be prepared for some accidents as many children like to remain babies themselves.

✓ Don't show any disgust for the child's faeces. She will regard using the potty as an achievement and will be proud of them. Children have no natural shame about their bodily functions (unless adults make them feel ashamed).

✓ Training pants, similar to ordinary pants but with a waterproof covering, are useful in the early stages of training – and having more than one potty in the house makes life easier.

✓ Always praise the child when she succeeds and do not show anger or disapproval if she doesn't – she may be upset by any accident herself.

✓ Offer the potty regularly so that the child becomes used to the idea of a routine, and get used to the signs that a child needs to use it.

✓ Encourage good hygiene right from the start, washing her hands after every visit to the potty.

✓ The child may prefer to try the 'big' toilet seat straight away; a toddler seat fixed onto the normal seat makes this easier.

Food hygiene and safety in the kitchen

Babies and young children are particularly vulnerable to gastro-enteritis or food poisoning. Food poisoning is often caused by poor hygiene in food preparation and storage. Food hygiene is essential for the prevention of food poisoning.

How bacteria enter food

Bacteria can enter food without causing the food to look, smell or even taste bad. Bacteria thrive in warm, moist foods, especially those rich in protein, such as meat and poultry (both cooked and raw), seafood, gravy, soup, cooked rice, milk, cream and egg dishes. Harmful bacteria multiply rapidly by dividing into two every 10 to 20 minutes, soon building up a colony of thousands which will cause poisoning.

To live and grow, bacteria must have:

▶ **Food** – especially the foods mentioned above;
▶ **Moisture** – fresh foods are more susceptible than dried foods;
▶ **Warmth** – they thrive most at body temperature (37°C)
▶ **Time** – bacteria reproduce rapidly in warm, moist food.

The prevention of food poisoning

1 Safe storage

✓ Keep food cold. The fridge should be kept as cold as it will go without actually freezing the food (1–5°C or 34–41°F). To be safe, use a fridge thermometer and open the door as few times as possible.
✓ Cool food quickly before placing in the fridge.
✓ Cover or wrap food with foodwrap or microwave clingfilm.
✓ Store raw foods at the bottom so that juices cannot drip onto cooked food.
✓ Freezers must be at a low enough temperature (−18°C or 0°F maximum).
✓ Never refreeze food which has begun to thaw.
✓ Label each item with the use by date.
✓ Thaw frozen meat completely before cooking.

2 Safe preparation and cooking

✓ Always wash hands in warm water and soap and dry on a clean towel:

• before handling food;
• after using the toilet;
• after touching raw food;
• after using a hankie; and
• after touching your face or hair.

✓ Never cough or sneeze over food.
✓ Always cover any septic cuts or boils with a waterproof dressing.
✓ Never smoke in any room that is used for food – it is illegal anyway.
✓ Keep clean, and wear clean protective clothing which is solely for use in the kitchen.
✓ Cook food thoroughly.
✓ Eggs should be cooked so that both the yolk and white are firm.
✓ Chicken must be tested to ensure that it is thoroughly cooked.
✓ Joints of meat and mince dishes must be cooked right through.
✓ Avoid cook-chill foods, which need very careful handling.

✓ Avoid having leftovers – they are a common cause of food poisoning.

✓ Do not re-heat food – even if it appears wasteful not to.

✓ If using a microwave oven:

- Do not reheat food by this method;
- Do not use for babies bottles;
- Always follow instructions and include 'standing time' to avoid burns;
- Keep the oven clean.

3 A safe kitchen

✓ Keep the kitchen clean – the floor, work surfaces, sink, utensils, cloths and waste bins should be cleaned regularly;

✓ Clean tin-openers, graters and mixers thoroughly after use.

✓ Tea towels should be boiled every day and dish cloths boiled or disinfected.

✓ Keep flies and other insects away – use a fine mesh over open windows.

✓ Keep pets away from the kitchen.

✓ Keep all waste bins covered, and empty them regularly.

✓ Stay away from the kitchen if you are suffering from diarrhoea or sickness.

Food-poisoning bacteria

Several types of bacteria can cause food poisoning (see Table 5.2), including the following:

- salmonella
- clostridium welchii
- clostridium botulinum
- listeria
- staphylococcus.

Multicultural aspects of food provision for babies

Food is an important part of any nursery environment and also an important part of the heritage of any culture. Britain is a multicultural society and one way of celebrating this fact is by embracing the food traditions of the different ethnic groups. The traditional British diet of lean meat, fresh vegetables and fresh fruit is a healthy one, but is in danger of being eroded by the introduction of fast foods which tend to be high in fat, salt and sugar.

Babies need to be introduced to a wide variety of foods from a range of different cultures. Providing good-quality food from the widest possible range of ethnically diverse diets has the following benefits:

Table 5.2　Food poisoning bacteria

Bacteria	Typically found in:	Symptoms	To reduce risk
Salmonella	Meat, poultry, raw eggs, meat pies and pasties, left-over food, unpasteurised milk	Starts suddenly 12 to 14 hours after eating; nausea, vomiting, abdominal pain and headache	Good personal hygiene; cook eggs well; avoid cross-infection from raw to cooked foods; cook food thoroughly
Clostridium Welchii	Meat, poultry, meat dishes, left-over food, gravy	Starts 8 to 18 hours after eating; diarrhoea, abdominal pain, no fever. Lasts 12 to 24 hours	Cook food thoroughly; heat to 100°C
Listeria	Chilled foods, e.g. soft cheeses and meat pâté	Starts 5 to 30 *days* after eating; 1 in 4 cases fatal; miscarriage, blood poisoning, meningitis; babies at risk	Avoid high-risk foods; avoid storing chilled foods for long periods; ensure proper re-heating
Clostridium Botulinum	Canned food not heated properly at time of canning; raw fish	Starts 12 to 36 hours after eating; often fatal; double vision; breathing difficulties	Avoid damaged or 'blown' cans; avoid keeping vacuum-packed fish in warm temperatures
Staphylococcus	Food that needs careful handling; custards and creams, cold desserts, sandwiches, unpasteurised milk	Starts 1 to 6 hours after eating; abdominal cramps, vomiting; lasts up to 24 hours	Good personal hygiene; avoid coughing and sneezing over food; avoid cross-infection from raw to cooked food; heat to 70°C for 15 minutes.

- it creates an awareness of different cultures;
- it promotes self-respect and respect for others;
- it affirms and values the sense of cultural identity in all children;
- it is enjoyable and a positive learning experience.

Traditional diets tend to use healthy ingredients in their staple dishes, such as:

- a wide variety of fresh vegetables;
- nuts, seeds and pulses;
- vegetable oils;
- unrefined starches and grains;
- fresh fish;
- quick stir-fry methods of cooking.

Staff in nurseries could ask parents of babies if they are willing to supply some favourite recipes for snacks and lunches; they may even wish to be further involved by coming into the nursery and cooking a particular dish. Nannies could ask the baby's parents if they could introduce a new taste from a different culture.

ACTIVITY 1

Bottle feeding

1   Find out the costs involved in bottle feeding a baby:

- the initial costs of equipment – sterilising unit, bottles, teats etc.
- the costs of formula milk and sterilising tablets for one year.

2   Collect some advertisements for baby milk formulas and analyse their appeal:

- make a poster using a selection of advertisements and discuss the similarities and differences between them;
- make a poster which 'sells' the idea of breast milk, using the same methods.

3   Discuss the problems faced by developing countries when large companies promote bottlefeeding by mounting campaigns and distributing free infant milk samples.

ACTIVITY 2

Weaning

Prepare a booklet for parents on weaning. Include the following information:

- when to start weaning a baby;
- what foods to start with;
- when and how to offer feeds;
- a weekly menu plan which includes vegetarian options.

Visit a store that stocks a wide variety of commercial baby foods and note their nutritional content e.g. protein, fat, energy, salt, sugar, gluten and additives. Make a chart that shows:

- the type of food e.g. rusks and cereals, savoury packet food, jars of sweet and savoury food;
- the average cost in each category;
- the packaging – note particularly if manufacturers use pictures of babies from different ethnic backgrounds.

If possible, ask a parent who has recently used weaning foods what reasons they had for choosing one product over another.

ACTIVITY 3

Multicultural food provision

Group activity: Divide into five groups of 3–5. Imagine you are working in a day nursery. Each group has been asked to plan an event to celebrate one of the following five festivals:

a) Chinese New Year
b) Jewish New Year
c) Easter
d) Id al Fitr (end of Ramadan)
e) Divali

Write a plan of the event to include the following:

- the food that is appropriate to the occasion;
- the activities that are appropriate to the occasion;
- the benefits to the babies and children of the event.

Sleep, Rest and Exercise

The need for sleep and rest

Everyone needs sleep, but the amount a baby sleeps varies enormously. The
length of time they spend sleeping will depend on the maturity of the brain
(the pre-term baby may sleep for long periods) and on the need for food.
Sleep is divided into two distinct states:

- rapid eye movement (REM), which is termed active sleep;
- non-rapid eye movement (NREM), which is termed quiet sleep.

In REM sleep the mind is active and is processing daytime emotional
experiences. In NREM sleep the body rests and restoration occurs. In babies
under one year, more of the sleep is active (REM). It is important not to
wake babies during NREM sleep, as it plays a vital part in restoring energy
levels. At first babies are likely to sleep in short bursts at any time during the
day or night. Most babies are able to sleep through normal household noises,
such as shutting doors, conversation or music. Some babies find droning
noises, such as washing machines or vacuum cleaners soothing.

Few aspects of parenthood are more stressful than months of broken nights.
Carers of babies could try the following strategies to encourage a different
sleep pattern between day and night:

> ► Allow the baby time to settle on her own so that she begins to
> develop her own way of going to sleep. Some babies do cry for a
> short period as they settle; leave her alone but stay within hearing
> distance and check after five minutes to see if she is comfortable.

> ▶ Give the baby plenty of stimulation by talking and playing with her when she is awake during the day.
> ▶ Try to make the night-time feeds as unstimulating as possible; feed, change and settle the baby in her cot.
> ▶ It is important that the baby learns to distinguish day from night. When it grows dark outside, close the curtains and turn the lights very low.
> ▶ Make bedtime at night into a routine; by repeating the same process each night, the baby feels secure and comfortable, both good aids to sleep.
> ▶ In cold weather, place a hot water bottle in the cot for a short while before putting the baby down, but **never** leave it with her in the cot.
> ▶ A night-light or dimmer switch enables you to check the baby during the night without waking her.

Establishing a bedtime routine

Between three and five months, most babies are ready to settle into a routine:

> ▶ Give the bath or wash and put on a clean nappy and nightwear;
> ▶ take her to say goodnight to other members of the household.;
> ▶ carry her into her room, telling her in a gentle voice that it is time for bed;
> ▶ give the last breast or bottlefeed in the room where the baby sleeps;
> ▶ sing a song or lullaby to help settle her, while gently rocking her in your arms;
> ▶ wrap her securely and settle her into the cot or cradle, saying goodnight;
> ▶ if she likes it, gently 'pat' her to sleep;
> ▶ some babies like the soothing sound of a musical mobile hung above the cot.

The routine can be adapted as the baby grows. In the early weeks, most mothers like to have the cot next to their bed; by about three to four months, the baby can be safely left in her own room.

SLEEPING OUTDOORS

Except when it's cold, a baby can sleep quite safely outdoors during the day, but make sure that she is warmly wrapped and visible at all times. Never place her carrycot in direct sunlight and always use a cat net over the carrycot; this will also protect her against insects.

Sleeping problems

A newborn baby spends most of her time sleeping, with brief intervals of wakefulness. Gradually she will settle into a pattern that usually involves a long nighttime sleep with shorter naps during the day. The most common problem often occurs at around six to nine months when babies are able to keep themselves awake on purpose. A baby who has not had the opportunity for fresh air, exercise and daytime stimulation is more likely to become irritable and develop a poor sleep pattern. This inability to settle to sleep sets up a vicious circle where the baby is miserable during the day, and then refuses to settle to sleep.

Comfort habits

Thumb sucking is a comfort habit that is totally within the baby's own control and is always available. Dummies are often useful for particularly 'sucky' babies but are best used only to help in settling a baby to sleep. Comfort objects, such as cuddly toys, dolls or old cot blankets, often become an essential part of a baby's life (see Chapter 3). Parents and carers find it helps to keep a spare 'cuddly' in case one should get lost or left behind on holiday; while the spare can never really replace the original object, it can provide some comfort to a distraught child.

Figure 6.1   Baby with comfort object

Sudden infant death syndrome (SIDS)

Sudden Infant Death syndrome is often called 'cot death'. It is the term applied to the sudden unexplained and unexpected death of an infant. The reasons for cot deaths are complicated and the cause is still unknown. Although cot death is the commonest cause of death in babies up to one year, it is still very rare, occurring in approximately two out of every 1000 babies. Recent research has identified various risk factors and the Foundation for the Study of Infant Deaths has written the following guidelines for parents:

> ► Place your baby on the back to sleep
> ► Cut smoking in pregnancy – fathers too!
> ► Do not let anyone smoke in the same room as your baby
> ► Do not let your baby get too hot or too cold
> ► Keep baby's head uncovered – place your baby in the 'feet to foot' position to prevent from wriggling under the covers (See Figure 6.2)
> ► If your baby is unwell, seek medical advice promptly

Side sleeping is not as safe as sleeping on the back, but it is much safer than sleeping on the front. Healthy babies placed on their backs are not more likely to choke. To prevent a baby wriggling down under the covers, place the baby's feet at the foot of the cot and make the bed up so that the covers reach no higher than the shoulders. Covers should be securely tucked in so that they cannot slip over the baby's head. Duvets or quilts, baby nests and pillows have the potential to trap air and may increase the risk of overheating.

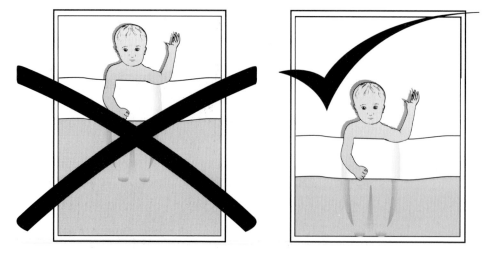

Figure 6.2   The Feet to Foot position

Guidelines for reducing the risk of cot death

> ▶ The room where a baby sleeps should be at a temperature which is comfortable for lightly clothed adults (16–20°C). If the baby is a natural tummy sleeper, keep turning her over and tuck in securely with blankets (as long as the weather is not too hot); a musical mobile may help to keep her happy while lying on her back.
> ▶ If the baby is snuffly or has a blocked nose, place a small pillow **under** the head end of the mattress, but make sure she does not slide down under the covers to the end of her cot.
> ▶ Never allow the baby to come into contact with smoky rooms; ask visitors not to smoke in the house. The risk factor increases with the number of cigarettes smoked.
> ▶ Learn to recognise the signs and symptoms of illness and how to respond.
> ▶ Use a room thermometer if necessary and check the baby's temperature by feeling her tummy, making sure your hands are warm beforehand.
> ▶ Babies over one month of age should **never** wear hats indoors, as small babies gain and lose heat very quickly through their heads.
> ▶ Learn and practise on a special baby resuscitation mannequin how to perform artificial ventilation and cardiac massage (see Chapter 7). **NB: This should always be practised under the supervision of a qualified first aider.**

The CONI support scheme

CONI (Care of the Next Infant) is a scheme developed by the Foundation for the Study of Infant Deaths to provide organised support for families who have suffered a loss of a child through cot death. Families who have suffered the loss of a baby in this way experience greater anxiety when expecting their next baby and the programme ensures that their baby will be under increased surveillance during the first few months of life and that extra support will be given if there is a problem. Parents are offered:

- weekly visits from their health visitor;
- the loan of an **apnoea monitor**, which records the baby's breathing movements or electronic scales for daily weighing – whichever they prefer;
- tuition in resuscitation skills and the significance of temperature, smoking and positioning the baby on the back;

- a daily diary to record symptoms;
- additional support from their family doctor (GP) and paediatrician.

CONI is usually offered to parents for a minimum of six months, or two months longer than the age at which their baby died.

The need for exercise

Babies need exercise in order to strengthen and develop their muscles. Exercise also helps to promote sleep as the body needs to relax after physical activity. Exercise strengthens and develops muscles. Carers of young babies can provide opportunities for exercise in the following ways:

- Give plenty of opportunity for the baby to practise each new aspect of development as she becomes capable of it.
- Allow times for wriggling on the floor without being hindered by nappy or clothes.
- Allow freedom to look around, to reach and to grasp.
- Give opportunities to roll, crawl and eventually walk around furniture safely.
- Provide objects and toys to exercise hand-eye co-ordination.
- After she has had her first triple vaccination, the baby can be taken to special baby sessions at the local swimming pool.

Handling small babies

A newborn baby may seem very fragile and vulnerable, but is really more robust than she appears. When picking up a very young baby, make eye contact and talk soothingly to her; any sudden noise or snatching movement will startle her. Until about four to eight weeks, babies are not able to control their head or muscles, so it is important that you always support the head, neck and spine when picking them up and when putting them down:

- slide one hand underneath her to support her lower back and bottom;
- slide your other hand under her neck and head;
- gently transfer her to a carrying or cradling position (see Figure 6.3 opposite).

Once the baby is old enough to support her own head, she will enjoy being hugged onto your shoulder, with her head nestling by your head and her bottom and legs supported by both your arms (see Figure 6.4 opposite).

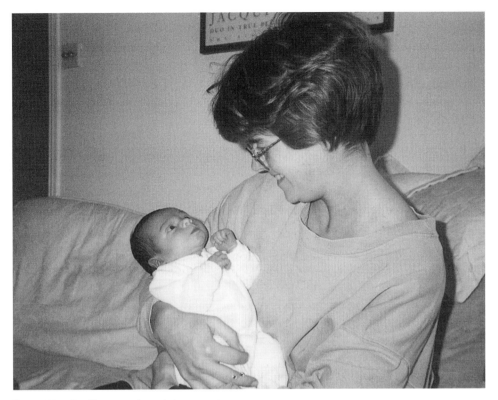

Figure 6.3   Cradling a newborn baby

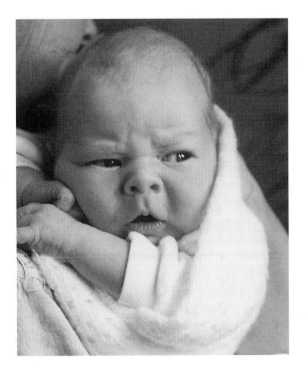

Figure 6.4   Shoulder hugging

How babies like to be held:

> ▶ cuddled up close to you;
> ▶ with your arm around her tummy, and her back against your body;
> ▶ upright looking over your shoulder, with her head supported;
> ▶ lying on top of your chest;
> ▶ cradled lengthways in your arms – an ideal position for smiling and talking to each other;
> ▶ cradled lengthways with the baby face down, with her chin and cheek resting on your forearm;
> **Most of all, babies need to have their heads and necks carefully supported**

Methods of carrying and transporting babies are discussed in Chapter 8.

Fresh air and sunlight

Babies benefit from being outside in the fresh air for a while each day. When air is trapped in a house it becomes stale, the level of humidity rises and there is an increased risk of infections spreading. Carers working in nurseries should ensure that rooms are well ventilated and that there are opportunities for babies to go outside. Sunlight is beneficial too, but care should be taken with babies and young children:

- Keep children out of the sun when it is at its most dangerous – between 11 am and 3 pm; carers of young children should plan outdoor activities to avoid this time.
- Specialists advise keeping babies of six to nine months out of the sun altogether to prevent the risk of developing skin cancer in later life.
- Use sun hats with a wide brim that will protect face, neck and shoulders on older babies.
- Use sun protection cream on all exposed areas.
- Use sun shades or canopies on buggies and prams.

Crying in young babies

Crying is a baby's way of expressing her needs; **babies never cry for no reason at all**, although in the first few weeks some babies cry from what appears to be a generalised feeling of discomfort as they adjust to life outside the womb. The average healthy baby cries for a total of three hours a day during the first three months. Finding out why a baby is crying is often a matter of elimination, so it is important that all carers should understand the

Table 6.1   Causes of crying

Hunger: This is the most common cause of crying. It is quite likely unless the baby has just been fed. Breast-fed and bottle-fed babies should be fed on demand in the early weeks. By the age of four months, the baby will probably need solid foods.

Being undressed: Most new babies hat being undressed and bathed, because they miss the contact between fabric and bare skin. One solution is to place a towel or shawl across the baby's chest and tummy when she is naked.

Discomfort: Until they can turn themselves over, babies rely on an adult to change their position; babies show marked preferences for sleeping positions.

Nappy needs changing: Some babies dislike being in a wet or dirty nappy and there may be nappy rash.

Twitches and jerks: Most new babies make small twitching and jerking movements as they are dropping off to sleep. Some babies are startled awake and find it difficult to settle to sleep because of these twitches. Wrapping a baby up firmly – or swaddling – usually solves the problem.

Over-tired or over-stimulated: Some babies can refuse to settle if there is too much bustle going on around them e.g. loud noises, too much bouncing or bright lights in a shopping centre; take her somewhere quiet and try rhythmical rocking, patting and generally soothing her.

Pain or illness: A baby might have a cold or snuffles and be generally fretful or may have an itchy rash, such as eczema. (For signs and symptoms of illness in babies, see page 140)

Allergy: An intolerance of cow's milk could cause crying; seek medical advice.

Thirst: In particularly hot weather, babies may be thirsty and can be given cool boiled water. Breastfed babies may be offered an extra feed as breast milk is a good thirst-quencher.

Feeling too hot or too cold: Temperature control is not well developed in the young baby; if too hot, she will look red in the face, feel very warm and may be sweaty around the neck folds; loosen clothes and wrappings and remove some layers of bedding, but watch for signs of chilling. If too cold, she may also have a red face or may be pale; to check, feel the hands, feet, tummy and the back of the neck; cuddle the baby, wrap a blanket around her and try a warm feed.

Boredom/need for physical contact: Babies find being cuddled or carried reassuring; talk to her and provide interesting objects for her to look at and a mobile; put pram under a tree or near a washing line so that she can see movements (NB: remember to fix a cat net to prevent insects and other unwanted visitors).

Colic: If the baby cries after being fed or has long bouts of crying especially in the evening, she may be suffering from colic (see Chapter 3 page 105).

Child abuse: A baby who has been abused in any way may cry and the carer should seek help from appropriate professionals.

physical and emotional needs of a baby at each stage of development. The way in which you respond to crying is important. Research has shown that those mothers who respond quickly to their baby's crying have babies who are contented and secure, whereas babies whose cries are ignored tend to cry even more.

Crying caused by pain

If a baby is fretful, off her food and generally miserable, she may be in some kind of pain. A short, spasmodic pain will usually produce bouts of distressed, shrill crying; a more continuos, generalised pain will produce a more grizzly, intermittent cry.

A high-pitched and persistent cry accompanied by drowsiness, floppy limbs, a bulging fontanelle (soft areas between the skull bones) or a rash, which does not disappear when pressed, can indicate a serious infection such as **meningitis** (see Chapter 7).

NB: Any crying which you think is caused by pain should be dealt with by taking the baby to the doctor without delay.

Persistent crying

Some babies do cry a great deal more than others and are difficult to soothe and comfort. Parents and carers can feel quite desperate through lack of sleep, personal problems and a baby who won't stop crying; they may suffer guilt at not being able to make their baby happy or lack confidence in caring for her. Such feelings of desperation and exhaustion can result in possible physical violence to the baby – throwing her into the cot, shaking her or even hitting her.

Guidelines: A help list for a crying baby

- ▶ Make sure the baby is not hungry or thirsty
- ▶ Check that the baby is not too hot or cold
- ▶ Check that the baby is not physically ill (see page 140 for signs of illness in babies)
- ▶ Check if the baby's nappy needs changing
- ▶ Treat colic or teething problems (see page 105)
- ▶ Cuddle the baby and try rocking her gently in your arms (Note: the most effective rate of rocking a young baby is at least 60 rocks a minute; the easiest way to achieve this rapid and soothing rocking without getting exhausted is to walk whilst rocking her from side to side)
- ▶ Rock the baby in a cradle or pram
- ▶ Talk and sing to the baby
- ▶ Take the baby for a walk or a car ride
- ▶ Leave the baby with someone else and take a break

- ▶ Play soothing music or a womb sounds recording
- ▶ Talk to a health visitor, GP or a parent's helpline
- ▶ Accept that some babies will cry whatever you do
- ▶ Remember that this phase will soon pass

If the crying ever feels too much to bear:

- ▶ Take a deep breath and let it out slowly. Put the baby down in a safe place, like a cot or a pram. Go into another room and sit quietly for a few minutes, perhaps with a cup of tea and the TV or radio on to help take your mind off the crying. When you feel calmer, go back to the baby.
- ▶ Ask a friend or relative to take over for a while
- ▶ Try not to get angry with the baby as she will instinctively recognise this and will probably cry even more
- ▶ Never let things get so bad that you feel desperate. There are lots of organisations that can help at the end of a telephone line.

Help and advice

Often just talking to others helps the carer to feel less isolated. Self-help groups such as Cry-sis, Parentline UK or the National Childbirth Trust Post-natal Support System can help by offering support from someone who has been through the same problem. Talking to the health visitor or GP may help, and some areas run clinics that help to devise a programme to stop the 'spiral' of helplessness.

Never shake a baby

A baby's head is big and heavy compared with the rest of her body. Unless supported, the head flops around because the neck muscles aren't yet strong enough to hold it still.

Shaking can cause serious, permanent injuries or even death

Shaking makes the head move back and forth very quickly and with great force. When this happens, tiny blood vessels can tear and bleed inside the baby's brain causing one or more of the following: blindness, deafness, seizures, learning difficulties, brain damage or even death.

WHY WOULD ANYONE SHAKE A BABY?

Some parents or carers may lose control and shake their baby in a moment of frustration or anger. This is particularly likely if the baby will not stop crying. Most people do not realise the damage that shaking can do; some may even think that it is preferable to smacking the baby.

It is never OK to shake or smack a baby

Activities relating to Chapter 6

ACTIVITY 1

Sudden Infant Death Syndrome

TASK ONE

In groups, prepare a display which details the risk factors implicated in Sudden Infant Death Syndrome. Using the information provided on page 122, make a poster for each risk factor and state clearly the precautions that should be taken to prevent cot death.

TASK TWO

In pairs, rehearse the procedure to follow if a young baby is found 'apparently lifeless' in his cot. Use a Resusci-baby and test each other's skills.

NB: Professional supervision will be required

ACTIVITY 2

Fresh air and sunlight

Write a short essay about the benefts of fresh air for babies. Mention the precautions you need to take in strong sunlight and general safety guidelines for caring for babies outdoors.

A C T I V I T Y   3

Crying in babies

Why do babies cry?

1   List the possible reasons why a baby may cry.
2   What actions might a parent or carer take when the baby is crying?
3   Where can parents and carers go to for advice if a baby will not stop crying?

Useful addresses and telephone numbers

Cry-sis 0171 404 5011
Offers counselling and practical advice on coping with persistent crying

Parentline UK 01702 559900
Runs a network of telephone helplines for parents under stress

NSPCC UK Child Protection Helpline 0800 800 500 FREEPHONE
Free 24 hour service offering counselling and advice for parents, carers and anyone concerned about a child at risk of abuse.

7

Care of the Ill Baby: Safety and First Aid Measures

Contents

Principles of disease transmission   Infection and immunity   Signs and symptoms of illness in babies   Failure to thrive   Common illnesses described   Care of the sick baby   Preparation for hospital admission   The role of professionals   Immunisation   Health promotion   First aid measures for accidents involving babies and young children: falls, head injuries, choking, burns and scalds, febrile convulsions, drowning, poisoning etc.

Infection

Infectious diseases are extremely common in childhood. An infection starts when certain micro-organisms enter the body and start to multiply. The body in turn reacts to this and uses various methods to try to destroy these micro-organisms. The illness which results is partly due to the effects of the multiplying micro-organisms and partly due to the body's reactions. Not all micro-organisms are **pathogenic** (causing disease in humans); pathogenic micro-organisms are also called **germs** and can only be seen with the aid of a powerful microscope. They may be sub-divided into:

- bacteria
- fungi
- viruses
- animal parasites
- protozoa

Bacteria

Bacteria are abundant almost everywhere – in the air, soil and water – and most are harmless to humans. Some bacteria indeed are beneficial – e.g. those that live in the intestine and help break down food for digestion. Pathogenic bacteria are classified, on the basis of shape, into four main groups:

- **Cocci** (spherical). Examples of diseases: pneumonia, tonsillitis, meningitis, bacterial endocarditis, toxic shock syndrome and various skin disorders.
- **Bacilli** (rod-shaped). Examples of diseases: tuberculosis, pertussis (whooping cough), tetanus, diphtheria, salmonellosis, and legionnaire's disease.
- **Vibrios** (curved shape). Example of disease: cholera.
- **Spirochaetes** (spiral shaped). Examples of diseases: syphilis, yaws, Lyme disease, and leptospirosis.

Each tiny bacterium consists of a single cell. The bacteria that colonise the human body thrive in warm, moist conditions. They reproduce by dividing into two cells, which in turn divide, and so on. Under ideal conditions (exactly the right temperature and sufficient nutrition for all cells) this division can take place every 20 minutes, resulting in a very rapid rate of reproduction. In a healthy child, such ideal conditions rarely occur and the body's **immune system** acts quickly to destroy the invading bacteria.

Viruses

Viruses are the smallest known type of pathogenic micro-organism and cannot be seen under an ordinary microscope. Viral infections range from the trivial – warts, the common cold, and other minor respiratory-tract infections – to mumps, measles and poliomyelitis, and to potentially very serious diseases, such as rabies, Lassa fever, AIDS (Acquired Immuno-Deficiency Disease). and possibly to various cancers.

Protozoa

All types of protozoa are simple one-celled animals and are of microscopic size. About 30 different types of protozoa are troublesome parasites of humans. Examples include: **amoebae** which cause diarrhoeal infections, the sexually transmitted infection trichomoniasis, malaria, and **toxoplasmosis** (a disease acquired from cats).

Fungi

Fungi are simple, parasitic life-forms including moulds, mildews, mushrooms and yeasts. Some fungi are harmlessly present all the time in areas of the body such as the mouth, skin, intestines and vagina, but are prevented from multiplying through competition from bacteria. Other fungi are dealt with by the body's immune system. Examples of fungal infection include thrush (candidiasis), athlete's foot and ringworm.

Animal parasites

Parasites are organisms that live in or on any other living creature. They obtain their food from the host's blood or tissues and are thus able to reproduce. Parasites may remain permanently with their host or may spend only part of their life cycles in association. Examples of parasites that commonly affect children are head lice, scabies mites, fleas and threadworm.

The transmission of infection

Infective micro-organisms cannot survive without their essential needs being met:

- warmth
- moisture
- food
- time

Some also require oxygen but others do not.

The chain of infection

All infection starts with:

1. The source

This may be:

> ▶ a person who is already infected with the disease;
> ▶ someone who is unaware of the existence of the disease but may be **incubating** it;
> ▶ a **carrier** of the disease, i.e. someone who has either had the disease and is convalescent, or who carries the causative organism with no adverse effects on themselves;
> ▶ household pets – e.g. cats and dogs may be the source of **streptococcal** infections, as well as of infestation by fleas and roundworms.

2. The reservoir

A reservoir of infection may exist which allows organisms to survive and multiply. Examples include:

- ▶ **dust**
- ▶ **organic matter** – e.g. food
- ▶ **secretions** – e.g. saliva, sputum and mucus
- ▶ **excretions** – e.g. urine and faeces
- ▶ **discharges** – e.g. pus from a wound or a boil
- ▶ **sinks, taps, waste pipes and drains**

3. Route of spread

Organisms may spread from the reservoir or source in a number of ways:

DIRECT INFECTION

- ▶ **Touch**: skin which is unbroken (i.e. no cuts or grazes) provides an effective barrier to most organisms, although diseases such as **impetigo** can be transferred onto skin already affected by **eczema**. **Scabies** is also spread by skin contact.
- ▶ **Droplet or airborne infection**: if a person coughs or sneezes without covering their nose and mouth, the droplets may be carried several metres and be inhaled by everyone else in the room; similarly, infection may be spread in this way by talking closely with others.
- ▶ **Kissing**: organisms are transferred directly from mouth to mouth; **glandular fever** (mononucleosis) is often referred to as the 'kissing disease'.
- ▶ **Injection**: the sharing of needles and syringes by drug addicts may cause infection to be transmitted by the blood. HIV infection and hepatitis B may both be transmitted in this way.
- ▶ **Sexual contact**: the transmission of diseases such as syphilis, gonorrhoea, HIV and non-specific genital infection (NSGI) is via sexual intercourse.

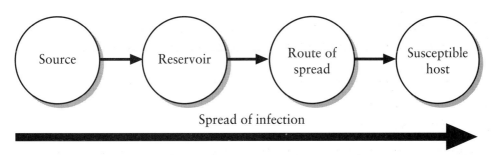

Figure 7.1   The chain of infection

INDIRECT INFECTION

▶ **Water**: the contamination of water used for drinking is a major method of spreading diseases e.g. typhoid fever, cholera, viral hepatitis A. Swimming in polluted water may cause ear infections. **Schistosomiasis** is a parasitic disease that afflicts over 200 million people world-wide; it is acquired by bathing in lakes and rivers infested by the **schistosome fluke**, which enters the human skin. Eating shellfish that live in polluted water may cause food poisoning or tapeworm infestations. Legionnaire's disease is a form of bacterial pneumonia caused by inhalation of water droplets from contaminated air-conditioning tanks.

▶ **Food**: animals that are kept or caught for food may harbour disease organisms in their tissues. If meat or milk from such an animal is taken without being thoroughly cooked or pasteurised, the organisms may cause illness in the human host, e.g. food poisoning.

▶ **Insects**: many types of fly settle first on human or animal excrement and then on food to lay eggs or to feed. Typhoid fever and food poisoning are two diseases spread in this way. Biting insects can spread serious infections through their bites. Examples include the mosquito (malaria and filariasis), the tsetse fly (African trypanosomiasis), the rat flea (plague) and the sand fly (leishmaniasis).

▶ **Rats**: rats may harbour the leptospirosis bacterium that is excreted in their urine and may be transmitted to humans. (Leptospirosis is also known as **Weil's disease**.)

Common childhood infections

The infection may be localised to one part of the body – e.g. **conjunctivitis** – or more widespread with manifestations in many of the body systems (e.g. **measles**).

INCUBATION PERIOD

This is the time gap between the entry of the micro-organisms into the body and the first appearance of **symptoms**. This period varies considerably with each infection; during the incubation period, the infected child is likely to pass on the micro-organism to others.

QUARANTINE PERIOD

This refers to the amount of time for which children who have been in

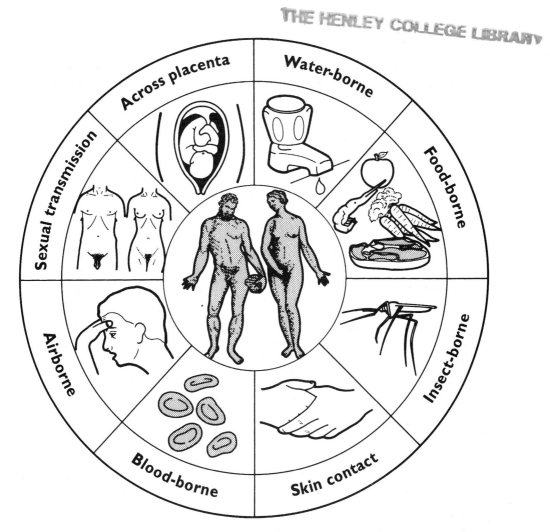

Figure 7.2   The spread of infection

contact with the disease are advised to remain at home or otherwise isolated. As some diseases are highly infective even when without symptoms (e.g. chickenpox), the quarantine period may have little relevance.

Fomites

Fomites (singular = fomes) are inanimate articles – such as clothing, books, toys, towels or a telephone receiver – which are not harmful in themselves but may harbour infection which can then be passed to another person. They are responsible particularly for the spread of respiratory infections and gastro-enteritis.

IMMUNITY

Immunity is the ability of the body to resist infection. When the body is attacked by bacteria there may be a **localised** reaction in the form of inflammation and a general response including fever. There is also a **specific immune response** when the body recognises the bacteria as foreign and produces **antibodies** (proteins with a protective role) which resist the particular bacteria.

THE INNATE IMMUNE SYSTEM

Almost everyone is born with an intact but undeveloped immune system that matures shortly after birth. This innate or non-specific immunity cannot guard against all disease-causing organisms; the growing child may encounter organisms that overcome these innate barriers and so cause disease. Figure 7.3 shows the external (physical and chemical) barriers to infection.

Breastfeeding

Breast milk contains antibodies that provide extra immunity until babies can form their own specific antibodies.

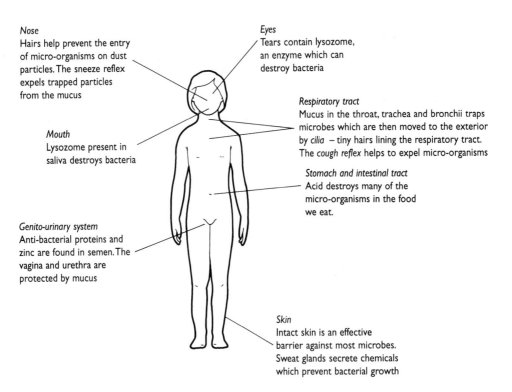

Nose
Hairs help prevent the entry of micro-organisms on dust particles. The sneeze reflex expels trapped particles from the mucus

Eyes
Tears contain lysozome, an enzyme which can destroy bacteria

Respiratory tract
Mucus in the throat, trachea and bronchii traps microbes which are then moved to the exterior by *cilia* – tiny hairs lining the respiratory tract. The *cough reflex* helps to expel micro-organisms

Mouth
Lysozome present in saliva destroys bacteria

Stomach and intestinal tract
Acid destroys many of the micro-organisms in the food we eat.

Genito-urinary system
Anti-bacterial proteins and zinc are found in semen. The vagina and urethra are protected by mucus

Skin
Intact skin is an effective barrier against most microbes. Sweat glands secrete chemicals which prevent bacterial growth

Figure 7.3   *Physical and chemical barriers to infection*

There are two types of immunity:

I **Active immunity** may be **natural** or **artificial**. Natural active immunity is acquired through:

  ▶ an attack of the disease in which the antibodies formed against it confer near life-long immunity. Rubella, measles and chickenpox are examples of such diseases.
  ▶ A sub-clinical infection in which the body defences are alerted, but where the attack by the organism is not strong enough to cause an acute attack of the illness.

Artificial active immunity is acquired through **immunisation** or inoculation with:

  • living organisms – e.g. vaccination against smallpox;
  • living weakened organisms – e.g. **BCG (Bacillus Calmette-Guerin** vaccine) against tuberculosis;
  • dead organisms – e.g. pertussis or whooping cough vaccine;
  • modified toxins or **toxoids** – e.g. the diphtheria vaccine

2 **Passive immunity** may also be natural or artificial. Natural passive immunity is possessed by babies in the first few months of life:

  ▶ antibodies are passed from mother to the foetus via the placenta; and
  ▶ in breast milk to the baby after birth.

Artificial passive immunity in which serum containing antibodies produced by a person who is convalescent from the disease is given to a child at risk of developing the disease; it gives immediate but short-lived protection.

Recognising illness in babies

The responsibility of caring for a baby who becomes ill is enormous; it is vital that carers should know the symptoms of illness and when to seek medical aid.

Signs and symptoms of illness

- **Raised temperature**
  The baby may look flushed or be pale, but will feel hot to the touch (Black babies may look paler than usual and the eyes may lose sparkle); occasionally a high temperature may trigger a seizure (fit) or febrile convulsion.
- **Diarrhoea**
  Persistent loose, watery or green stools can quickly dehydrate a baby.
- **Excessive and persistent crying**
  If the baby cannot be comforted in the usual way or if the cry is very different from usual cries.
- **Dry nappies**
  If her nappies are much drier than usual because she has not passed urine, this may indicate dehydration.
- **Difficulty with breathing**
  If breathing becomes laboured or noisy with a cough, the baby may have bronchitis or croup.
- **Sunken anterior fontanelle**
  A serious sign of dehydration, possibly after diarrhoea and vomiting.

- **Loss of appetite**
  The baby may refuse feeds or take very little; an older baby may only want milk feeds and refuse all solids.
- **Vomiting**
  If persistent or projectile in nature and not the more usual possetting.
- **Lethargy** or 'floppiness'
  The baby may appear to lack energy and lack the normal muscle tone.
- **Persistent coughing**
  Coughing in spasms lasting more than a few seconds; long spasms often end with vomiting.
- **Discharge from the ears**
  Ear infections may not show as a discharge but the baby may pull at her ears and may have a high temperature.
- **Seizures** (also called convulsions or fits)
  During a seizure a baby either goes stiff or else jerks her arms or legs for a period lasting up to several minutes. Her eyes may roll up, she may go blue, may dribble and will be unresponsive to you.

Role of the carer

When any child is unwell, the carer should proceed as follows:

1 **Inform the next-of-kin**: always make sure you have a contact number
2 **Seek medical advice.** This may be the family doctor; or, in an emergency, **phone 999** for an ambulance and inform the next-of-kin as soon as is practicable.

3 **Stay with the baby at all times**: you will be able to report on any examinations carried out and will be a reassuring presence to the baby.
4 **Observe the baby carefully** and note any changes; record her temperature (see page 145) and take steps to reduce a high temperature (see below).
5 **Give extra fluids if possible** and carry out routine skin care. The baby may want extra physical attention or prefer to rest in her cot.

Meningitis

Meningitis is an inflammation of the lining of the brain. It is a very serious illness, but if it's detected and treated early, most children make a full recovery. The early symptoms of meningitis such as fever, irritability, restlessness, vomiting and refusing feeds are also common with colds and 'flu. A baby with meningitis can become seriously ill within hours. The important signs to look out for in babies are:

- fever with cold hands and feet
- high-pitched, moaning cry or whimpering
- red or purple spots that do not fade under pressure – do the 'Glass Test' (see below)
- neck retraction with an arched back
- refusing feeds or being sick
- being fretful and not liking being picked up
- blank and staring expression
- difficult to wake and has no energy

The 'Glass Test': Press the side of a glass firmly against the rash – you will be able to see if it fades and loses colour under the pressure. If it doesn't change colour, contact a doctor immediately.

Principles of caring for sick babies

Small children sometimes cannot explain their symptoms, and display non-specific complaints such as headache, sleeplessness, vomiting or inability to stand up. Babies have even less certain means of communication, and may simply cry strangely, refuse feeds or become listless and lethargic. In most infectious illnesses, there will be fever.

Fever

Known medically as **pyrexia**, a fever is defined as a body temperature above 37°C. The only way to tell if a baby has a high fever is to take her temperature with a thermometer.

Table 7.1 Illnesses in babies

Condition (and cause)	Signs and symptoms	Role of the carer
Common cold (coryza) (virus)	Runny nose, sneeze; tiny babies may have breathing problem.	Keep nose clear. Give small frequent feeds. Nasal drops if prescribed.
Cough (usually virus)	Often follows on from a cold; may be a symptom of other illness, e.g. measles.	Keep air moist. Check the baby has not inhaled an object. Give medicine if prescribed.
Croup (virus)	Croup is an infection of the voice box or larynx, which becomes narrowed and inflamed. Barking cough (like sea lions), noisy breathing, distressed; usually occurs at night.	If severe, seek medical help. Reassure her and sit her up. Keep calm and reassure the baby. Inhaling steam may also benefit some babies. You can produce steam by boiling a kettle, running the hot taps in the bathroom, using a room humidifier or putting wet towels over the radiator. If using steam, take care to avoid scalding.
Bronchiolitis (virus)	A harsh dry cough which later becomes wet and chesty; runny nose, raised temperature, wheeze, breathing problems, poor feeding or vomiting. May develop a blue tinge around the lips and on the fingernails (known as cyanosis).	Observe closely. Seek medical help if condition worsens. Increase fluids. Give small regular feeds. Give prescribed medicine. Comfort and reassure.
Febrile convulsions (high temperature)	Convulsions caused by a high temperature (over 39 degrees centigrade, 102 degrees fahrenheit) or fever are called febrile convulsions. Baby will become rigid, then the body may twitch and jerk for one or two minutes.	Try not to panic. Move potentially harmful objects out of the way and place the baby in the recovery position. Loosen clothing. Call doctor. Give tepid sponging. Comfort and reassure.
Meningitis (virus or bacteria)	Raised temperature, may have a blotchy rash. May refuse feeds, have a stiff neck, have a seizure. Bulging fontanelles, may have a shrill, high-pitched cry.	Seek medical help urgently. Reduce temperature. Reassure.

Table 7.1 (continued)

Condition (and cause)	Signs and symptoms	Role of the carer
Otitis media (virus or bacteria)	Will appear unwell; may have raised temperature. May vomit, may cry with pain. May have discharge from ear.	Take to doctor, give antibiotics and analgesics (or painkillers). Increase fluids; comfort and reassure.
Conjunctivitis (virus or bacteria)	Inflammation of the thin, delicate membrane that covers the eyeball and forms the lining of the eyelids. Symptoms include a painful red eye, with watering and sometimes sticky pus.	Take to doctor who may prescribe antibiotic eye drops or ointment. Bathe a sticky eye gently with cool boiled water and clean cotton wool swabs. Always bathe the eye from the inside corner to the outside to avoid spreading infection.
Colic	This occurs in the first 12 weeks. It causes sharp, spasmodic pain in the stomach, and is often at its worst in the late evening. Symptoms include inconsolable high-pitched crying, drawing her legs up to her chest, and growing red in the face.	Try to stay calm! Gently massage her abdomen in a clockwise direction, using the tips of your middle fingers. Sucrose solution (3 × 5 ml teaspoons of sugar in a cup of boiling water and left to cool) is said to have a mild pain-killing effect on small babies. Dribble 2 ml of this solution into the corner of the baby's mouth twice a day. If the problem persists, contact the doctor.
Diarrhoea	Frequent loose or watery stools. Can be very serious in young babies, especially when combined with vomiting, as it can lead to severe dehydration.	Give frequent small drinks of cooled, boiled water containing glucose and salt or a made-up sachet of rehydration fluid. If the baby is unable to take the fluid orally, she must be taken to hospital urgently and fed intravenously, by a 'drip'. If anal area becomes sore, treat with a barrier cream.
Gastro-enteritis (virus or bacteria)	The baby may vomit and usually has diarrhoea as well; often has a raised temperature and loss of appetite. May show signs of abdominal pain i.e. drawing up of legs to chest and crying.	Reassure baby. Observe strict hygiene rules. Watch out for signs of dehydration. Offer frequent small amounts of fluid, and possibly rehydration salts. Prevention (see page 165).
Neonatal cold injury – or hypothermia	The baby is cold to the touch. Face may be pale or flushed. Lethargic, runny nose, swollen hands and feet. Pre-term infants and babies under 4 months are at particular risk.	Warm *slowly* by covering with several light layers of blankets and by cuddling. No direct heat. Offer feeds high in sugar and seek medical help urgently.

Table 7.1 (continued)

Condition (and cause)	Signs and symptoms	Role of the carer
Reflux	Also known as gastro-intestinal reflux (GIR) or gastro-oesophageal reflux (GOR). The opening to the stomach is not yet efficient enough to allow a large liquid feed through. Symptoms include grizzly crying and excessive **possetting** after feeds.	Try feeding the baby in a more upright position and bring up wind by gently rubbing her back. After feeding leave the baby in a semi-sitting position. Some doctors prescribe a paediatric reflux suppressant or antacid mixture to be given before the feed.
Tonsillitis (virus or bacteria)	Very sore throat, which looks bright red. There is usually fever and the baby will show signs of distress from pain on swallowing and general aches and pains. May vomit.	Encourage plenty of fluids – older babies may have ice lollies to suck. Give pain relief, e.g. paracetamol. Seek medical aid if no improvement and if fever persists.

Table 7.2 When to call the doctor

When to call the doctor
If you think the baby's life is in danger, dial **999** if you are in the UK, ask for an ambulance urgently and explain the situation. Contact the family doctor (GP) if the baby has any of the following symptoms. If the doctor cannot reach you quickly, take the baby to accident and emergency department of the nearest hospital:

• Has a temperature of 38.6°C (101.4°F) which is not lowered by measures to reduce **fever**, or a temperature over 37.8°C (100°F) for more than one day.	• Has **convulsions**, or is limp and floppy.
• Has severe or persistent **vomiting** and/or **diarrhoea**, seems dehydrated or has projectile vomiting.	• **Cannot be woken**, is unusually drowsy or may be losing consciousness.
• Has symptoms of **meningitis**.	• Has **croup** symptoms.
• Is pale, listless and **does not respond** to usual stimulation.	• **Cries or screams** inconsolably and may have severe **pain**.
• Has bulging **fontanelle** (soft spot on top of head) when not crying.	• Appears to have severe abdominal pain, with symptoms of **shock**.
• **Refuses** two successive feeds.	• Develops **purple-red rash** anywhere on body.
• Passes bowel motions (stools) containing **blood**.	• Has **jaundice**.
• Has a suspected **ear infection**.	• Has been **injured**, e.g. by a burn which blisters and covers more than of 10% the body surface.
• Has inhaled something, such as a peanut, into the air passages and may be **choking**.	• Has swallowed a **poisonous** substance, or an object, e.g. a safety pin or button.
• Has bright pink cheeks and swollen hands and feet (could be due to **hypothermia**).	• Has difficulty in **breathing**.

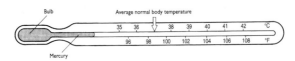

Figure 7.4   A clinical thermometer

TAKING A BABY'S TEMPERATURE

All family first aid kits should contain a thermometer. This may be:

- **a clinical thermometer**: a glass tube with a bulb at one end containing mercury. This tube is marked with gradations of temperature in degrees Centigrade and Fahrenheit.

When the bulb end is placed under the baby's armpit or in the groin fold, the mercury will expand and so move up the tube until the temperature of the baby's body is reached.

1   Check that the silvery column of mercury is shaken down to 35 degrees centigrade.
2   Place the bulb end of the thermometer in the baby's armpit, holding her arm close to her side for two minutes.
3   Remove the thermometer, and holding it horizontally and in a good light, read off the temperature measured by the level of the mercury. Record the time and the temperature reading.
4   After use, wash the thermometer in tepid water, and shake the column of mercury down again to 35 degrees Centigrade. Dry carefully and replace in case.

NB: A clinical thermometer should never be placed in a baby's mouth, because of the danger of biting and breaking the glass.

- **Digital thermometer**: this is battery-operated and consists of a narrow probe with a tip sensitive to temperature. It is easy to read via a display panel and unbreakable.

1   Place the narrow tip of the thermometer under the baby's arm as described above.
2   Read the temperature when it stops rising; some models beep when this point is reached.

- **Plastic fever strip**: this is a rectangular strip of thin plastic which contains temperature sensitive crystals that change colour according to the temperature measured. It is not as accurate as the other thermometers but is a useful check.

1 Hold the plastic strip firmly against the baby's forehead for about 30 seconds.
2 Record the temperature revealed by the colour change.

Other signs that indicate fever are:

- the baby may appear 'feverish' – red, hot cheeks and bright, glittery eyes;
- the baby will usually be reluctant to feed;
- the baby will usually appear fretful or restless, or may sleep a lot.

Whatever the **cause** of the high temperature, it is important to try to reduce it, as there is always the risk of a fever leading to **convulsions** or **fits**.

Febrile convulsions

Convulsions caused by a high temperature (over 39°C, 102°F) or fever are called febrile convulsions. Febrile convulsions are quite common and one in 20 children has at least one during childhood. They occur mainly in children between the ages of six months and five years when the temperature rises too quickly for the child's immature temperature-lowering mechanism in the brain to cope. This can happen if the child has an illness such as measles, whooping cough or middle ear infection (**otitis media**). The sudden rise in temperature causes the brain cells to discharge electrical impulses to the muscles which then contract or go into spasm. Some young babies may not twitch or lose consciousness but stare without blinking, or stop breathing for a short time and go blue.

In some families there is a history of febrile convulsions. For treatment of febrile convulsions, see Table 7.1, page 142.

Bringing down a high temperature/reducing a fever

▶ Offer cooled boiled water and encourage the baby to drink as much fluid as possible.
▶ Sponge her down, using tepid water (see below) – or give her a cool bath.
▶ Give her the correct dose of paracetamol syrup. Follow the instructions on the bottle carefully.*
▶ Try to cool the air in the baby's room – use an electric fan or open the window.
▶ Reassure the baby who may be very frightened. Remain calm

yourself and try to stop the baby crying as this will tend to push the temperature higher still.
▶ If the temperature will not come down, then call the doctor.

NB: Always consult a doctor if a high fever is accompanied by symptoms such as severe headache with stiff neck, abdominal pain or pain when passing urine.

Tepid sponging to reduce a temperature

▶ Make sure the air in the room is comfortably warm – not hot, cold or draughty.
▶ Lay the baby on a towel on your knee or on the bed and gently remove her clothes; reassure her by talking gently.
▶ Sponge her body, limbs and face with tepid or lukewarm water – not cold; as the water evaporates from the skin, it absorbs heat from the blood and so cools the system.
▶ As the baby cools down, pat her skin dry with a soft towel and dress her only in a nappy; cover her with a light cotton sheet.
▶ Keep checking her condition to make sure that she does not become cold or shivery; if she does become cold, put more light covers over her.
▶ If the temperature rises again, repeat sponging every 10 minutes.

Giving medicine

Written permission must always be obtained from the baby's parent or next-of-kin before you give any medicine to the baby. Oral medicine is usually dispensed in liquid form (elixir or suspension) and may be given to the baby by spoon or dropper. When giving a baby medicine:

▶ Always check the label on the bottle and the instructions. If it has been prescribed by the doctor, check that it is for the baby and follow the instructions exactly.
▶ Shake the bottle before measuring the dose. Always pour any medicine bottle with the label uppermost so that the instructions remain legible if the medicine runs down the side of the bottle
▶ Put a bib on the baby and have some baby wipes or a flannel close at

> ▶ hand to wipe clean. Cradle the baby as if bottlefeeding, with her head tilted back.
> ▶ Use a 5 ml medicine spoon to measure the dose; if using a dropper, measure the dose in a 5 ml spoon and then suck it up with the dropper.
> ▶ Spoon or squeeze the dose into the baby's mouth.

Failure to thrive

Failure to thrive (FTT) can be defined as a failure to gain weight at the expected rate. The first issue to be explored if a baby appears to be under-nourished is feeding; often a newly-weaned baby will fail to thrive (or gain weight) due to intolerance of a newly-introduced feed. Once the food is withdrawn from the diet, the baby will usually thrive. There may be other problems associated with feeding a young baby, such as breathing difficulties or a poor sucking reflex in a premature baby. A baby who is vomiting frequently over a period of time is also unlikely to thrive. Vomiting may be the result of **pyloric stenosis**, **gastro-enteritis** or **whooping cough (pertussis)**.

Preparing for hospital admission

The majority of admissions to hospital in the birth to 18 months age group will be emergency admissions that cannot be planned for. Occasionally babies *do* have to be admitted to hospital for investigations or treatment and it is understood that the best place for babies and toddlers is by their parents' side. Hospitals now encourage parents to remain by their child's bedside throughout their hospital stay. Often the experience is just as stressful for the parents, particularly if they have their own childhood memories of hospitalisation. Guidelines for early years workers are:

> ▶ If possible, arrange to visit the ward a few days before admission – most wards welcome such visits and are happy to talk with carers. (Many fears are based on ignorance – fear of the unknown.)
> ▶ Arrange care for any other children in the family; the baby is a priority as she is having to cope with new faces and new experiences and needs her parent now more than at any other time.
> ▶ Try to be involved in the baby's care as fully as possible.
> ▶ Take the baby's favourite toy or 'comforter' as a link with home.
> ▶ Tell the ward staff about the baby's and sleeping patterns and preferences.

Child health promotion

Child health promotion is a programme of care managed by professionals – family doctors, nurses, health visitors and other members of the primary health-care team. It has four main aims:

* to promote good health and development;
* to prevent illness, accidents and child abuse;
* to recognise, and where possible, to eradicate potential problems affecting development, behaviour and education;
* to detect abnormality, in order to offer investigation and treatment.

Primary prevention includes:

* good nutrition (see Chapter 5);
* good dental care (see Chapter 4);
* the prevention of childhood accidents (see Chapter 8);
* immunisation against childhood diseases.

Primary prevention: immunisation

In the past ten years there has been a dramatic reduction in the incidence of common childhood illnesses, due to:

* greater public awareness of the availability of immunisation;
* the introduction of two major new vaccines – MMR and Hib.;
* government policy which has led to national strategies on immunisation and better uptake.

Immunisation schedules vary very slightly between different Health Districts, but the schedule currently recommended by the Department of Health is shown in Table 7.5.

The range and purpose of immunisation programmes

Immunisations are carried out in child health clinics. The doctor will check that the child has had the relevant immunisations and will discuss any fears the parents may have about particular vaccines. No vaccine is completely risk-free and parents are asked to sign a consent form prior to immunisations being given. Immunisations are only given if the child is well and may be postponed if the child has had a reaction to any previous immunisation or if the child is taking any medication that might interfere with their ability to fight infection.

The effects of the disease are usually far worse than any side effects of a vaccine.

Table 7.3   Immunisation schedules

When is the immunisation due?	Which immunisations	Type
At two months	Polio	By mouth
	Hib Diphtheria Tetanus Whooping cough	One injection
At three months	Polio	By mouth
	Hib Diphtheria Tetanus Whooping cough	One injection
At four months	Polio	By mouth
	Hib Diphtheria Tetanus Whooping cough	One injection
At 12 to 15 months	Measles Mumps Rubella	One injection
3 to 5 years (usually before the child starts school)	Measles Mumps Rubella	One injection
	Diphtheria Tetanus	One injection
	Polio	By mouth
10 to 14 years (sometimes shortly after birth)	BCG (against tuberculosis)	Skin test followed by one injection if needed
School leavers 13 to 18 years	Diphtheria Tetanus	One injection
	Polio	By mouth

THE HIB VACCINE

From 1992 an immunisation against **haemophilus influenzae type b (Hib)** has been offered to all children under 4 years old. Hib is a bacterium that causes a range of illnesses:

* meningitis (inflammation of the **meninges** surrounding the brain (see page 141);

- epiglottitis – a severe form of croup;
- septicaemia (blood poisoning);
- septic arthritis and osteomyelitis (infections in bones and joints);
- pneumonia.

Children under four years are most at risk with the peak incidence of Hib infection being among babies of 10–11 months. The Hib bacteria normally live in the nose and throat and are spread in the same way as coughs and colds (i.e. by the droplet/airborne route).

NB: The Hib vaccine does not protect against other types of meningitis (meningococcal, pneumococcal or viral) or against viral infections such as 'flu.

THE MMR (MEASLES, MUMPS AND RUBELLA) VACCINE

This combined injection replaced the measles vaccine and has reduced the serious complications that often follow an attack of these diseases in childhood. Mumps is often thought to be a mild illness but it is the most common cause of viral meningitis in children, and can cause permanent deafness.

Most children are perfectly well after having the MMR vaccine. However, it is quite common for children to develop a mild fever and a rash, a week to ten days later, which usually only lasts two to three days. A few children get swollen faces or a mild form of mumps about three weeks after immunisation. Any swelling will gradually go down and none of these reactions are infectious. Serious reactions to the MMR vaccine (such as fever or encephalitis) are extremely rare and are far more likely to occur as a result of having the diseases themselves.

Secondary prevention: child health surveillance

All parents are issued with a Personal Child Health Record that enables them to keep a record of their child's development. This is completed by doctors, health visitors and parents and is a useful source of information if the child is admitted to hospital or is taken ill when the family are away from home.

The importance of early detection

Parents want to know about their child's problems as soon as possible; it is easier to come to terms with a serious problem in a young baby than in an older child. Health professionals should always take the parent's worries seriously and never assume that parents are fussy, neurotic or over-anxious. Early years workers are usually very astute in recognising abnormalities in development because of their experience with a wide variety of children.

Development is usually reviewed under the following headings:

- **gross motor skills**: sitting, standing, walking, running;
- **fine motor skills**: handling toys, stacking bricks, doing up buttons and tying shoe-laces (gross manipulative and fine manipulative skills);
- **speech and language** – including hearing;
- **social behaviour**.

Early detection is important:

- early treatment may reduce or even avoid permanent damage in some conditions;
- an early diagnosis may allow **genetic counselling** and so avoid the birth of another child with a disabling condition.

SCREENING

The aim of a screening programme is to examine all children at risk from a certain condition; the term **screening** refers to the examination of apparently healthy children to distinguish those who probably have a condition from those who probably do not. Hearing defects are often detected in this way at one of the routine checks carried out at the Child Surveillance Clinic.

NEONATAL EXAMINATION

All babies are examined as soon as possible after birth – see Chapter 2.

THE SIX-TO-EIGHT-WEEK CHECK

This check usually takes place in the child health clinic. The doctor will enquire about any parental concerns:

- feeding;
- sleeping;
- bowel actions;
- micturition: the act of passing urine

OBSERVATION

While the parent is undressing the baby for examination, the doctor will look out for:

- the responsiveness of the baby – smiles, eye contact, attentiveness to parent's voice etc.
- any difficulties the parent has with holding the baby – e.g. a depressed mother will lack visual attention and may not give a good supporting hold;
- jaundice, anaemia.

Measurement

- The baby is weighed naked and the weight plotted on the growth chart (see page 54).
- The head circumference is measured and plotted on the growth chart.

Examination

This examination follows the lines of the examination at birth (see Chapter 2 page 27):

- The general appearance of the baby will give an indication of whether the child is well nourished.
- The eyes are inspected using a light – the baby will turn their head and follow a small light beam; an **ophthalmoscope** is used to check for a **cataract**.
- The heart is **auscultated** i.e. listened to with a **stethoscope**, to exclude any **congenital defect**.
- The hips are manipulated again to exclude the presence of congenital dislocation of the hips.
- The baby is placed prone and will turn her head to one side; hands are held with the thumbs inwards and the fingers wrapped around them.
- The posterior fontanelle is usually closed by now; the anterior fontanelle does not close until around eighteen months.

Hearing

There is no specific test at this age; the parent is asked if they think the child can hear. A baby may startle to a sudden noise or freeze for some sounds.

The doctor will discuss health topics and give the first immunisation and finally complete the Personal Child Health Record.

Health education points at 0–8 weeks

- **Nutrition**: breastfeeding, preparation of formula feeds, and specific feeding difficulties.

- **Immunisation**: discuss any concerns and initiate a programme of vaccination.
- **Passive smoking**: babies here are at risk of respiratory infections and **middle ear disease**.
- **Illness in babies**: how to recognise symptoms.
- **Crying**: coping with frustration and tiredness.
- **Reducing the risk of cot death**: (Sudden Infant Death Syndrome).
- **Accident prevention**: see pages 180–184.

The six-to-nine-month check

The doctor or health visitor will enquire again about any parental concerns.

OBSERVATION

- Socialisation and attachment behaviour;
- visual behaviour;
- communication – sounds, expressions and gestures;
- motor development – sitting, balance, use of hands, any abnormal movement patterns.

MEASUREMENT

- Head circumference and weight – plotted on growth chart

EXAMINATION

- Manipulation of the hips is carried out.
- The heart is auscultated.
- The testes are checked in boys.
- The eyes are checked for a squint – if this is present, the child is referred to an ophthalmologist (eye specialist); visual behaviour is checked;
- Hearing is tested by the **distraction test** – see below.

The distraction test

All babies should have a competently performed distraction test for hearing at 7–8 months. It is essential that the test is carried out in a quiet room and that two trained professionals be involved. The timing of the test is important, since by 8 months of age, 95% of babies have acquired the ability to localise a sound correctly, in any position except directly behind or above the head.

The aim of the test is to see if the baby hears sounds of varying sound and pitch. The baby should be alert and well and have adequate head control.

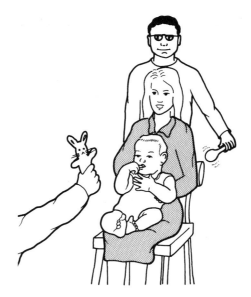

Figure 7.5　The distraction test

The baby is placed on the parent's lap facing the distractor, supported round the waist but held well away from the parent (see Figure 7.5).

The **distractor** holds the baby's attention with a gently moving toy. When the baby's attention is riveted on the toy, the distractor reduces the stimulation by covering or removing the toy, but does not let the baby handle it.

The **tester** presents sound stimuli at a distance of one metre from the baby's ear, on the same horizontal plane and at a sufficient angle so that the baby cannot see the tester. The **test sounds** must be quiet and presented randomly and the object is to demonstrate two high frequency and two low-frequency responses. High frequency sounds are usually made using a Nuffield rattle and saying 'sss' as in bus. Low frequency sounds are made using 'ooooo' as in shoe – hummed, not whispered.

If the baby 'fails' the distraction test, the health visitor will usually arrange to repeat the test about one month later; if the test is failed again, the baby will be referred to an **audiologist** (a person trained to assess hearing).

Health education points
- **Nutrition**: weaning, control of sugar intake.
- **Immunisations**: check they are up to date,

- **Teeth**: regular brushing once teeth appear; information on fluoride; visit the dentist;
- The need for **play** and **language stimulation**
- **Accident prevention** – see pages 180–184.

The use of charts in child health surveillance

Many methods have been devised to record growth and development in a systematic manner; none of them alone provides a diagnosis. Their aim is to assist in the detection of those children who need further examination. The early years worker is in an ideal position to be able to notice if a child is not making progress in any area of development; continuous, structured observation is the most effective tool for assessing development and any cause for concern should be noted and referred to the health visitor and/or the paediatrician. Apart from the widely used Growth Charts (see Chapter 2), health clinics use a variety of developmental scales and charts to chart baby development:

Gesell Developmental Schedules (1969)

Most developmental scales are based on the work of American developmental psychologist Arnold Gesell in the 1940s. Gesell's team studied hundreds of children in a fabric observation dome which was brightly lit inside so that the child would be unaware of the students, parents and cameraman observing from outside. A series of tests was carried out using wooden blocks, cups and bells. At 15 months a child will build a tower of two blocks; at 4 years, a tower of 10 blocks. 'Normal' development is defined in relation to other children rather than to a fixed external standard.

The scales are strongly biased toward **motor** development in the first two years, but the overall results are presented in four areas: **motor**, **adaptive**, **language** and **personal-social**.

Denver Developmental Screening Test

The Denver Test is widely used by paediatricians and health visitors to record a child's all-round development in the first year. Those recording the information should be very familiar with child development and what is 'normal' at any age. The Test provides useful information about the range of ages at which different abilities are usually acquired.

BAYLEY SCALES OF INFANT DEVELOPMENT

Developed by N. Bayley in 1965, these are widely used for infants of 2 months to 2.5 years; there are three complementary parts: the mental scale, the motor scale and the infant behaviour record.

There are many other tests, scales and centile charts in use in child health clinics and hospitals.

Notifiable diseases

Some diseases are notifiable by law to the Medical Officer for Environmental Health. In England and Wales, they are:

Acute encephalitis	Mumps
Acute meningitis	Ophthalmia neonatorum
Acute poliomyelitis	Paratyphoid fever
Anthrax	Plague
Cholera	Rabies
Diphtheria	Relapsing fever
Dysentery	Rubella
Food poisoning (all sources)	Scarlet fever
Infective jaundice	Small pox
Lassa fever	Tetanus
Leprosy	Tuberculosis
Leptospirosis	Typhoid fever
Malaria	Typhus
Marburg disease	Viral haemorrhagic fever (e.g. Ebola fever)
Measles	Whooping cough
Meningococcal septicaemia	Yellow fever

Medicines

Every home should have a properly stocked medicine cabinet, preferably locked but always out of reach to children. The cabinet should contain:

* A pain reliever such as paracetamol. The doses for children of different ages should be on the bottles.
* A hot-water bottle – when wrapped in a towel it can relieve the pain of an aching abdomen or bruised joint.
* A kaolin mixture for the relief of simple diarrhoea.

- Zinc and castor oil cream – for nappy rashes.
- Calamine lotion – for itchy spots and rashes.
- A clinical thermometer/digital thermometer/fever strip.
- A teething ring (if appropriate).
- A measuring spoon or glass for liquid medicines.
- A small packet of cotton wool.
- A pack of assorted fabric plasters and one of hypo-allergenic plasters.
- Crêpe bandages and conforming bandages.
- A small bottle of liquid antiseptic or antiseptic spray.
- Arnica cream – useful for bruises.
- Any necessary prescription drugs.

Before stocking the medicine cabinet, discard all the half-empty, improperly labelled bottles and any medicines that are over 6 months old. Keep down costs by buying non-branded products.

Administration of medicines

Most medicines for babies are made up as a syrup or an elixir and are pleasantly flavoured to make them easy to swallow.

- If tablets or capsules are prescribed, these may be crushed between two spoons and given in fruit juice, jam or honey.
- Antibiotics may be prescribed for any infection or to prevent secondary infection (these sometimes cause diarrhoea). **NB: Some antibiotics may need to be kept in the 'fridge.**
- When a course of antibiotics is prescribed it is vital that all the tablets/medicines are given, even if the child makes a speedy recovery.

NB: Permission must always be obtained from the child's parent or guardian before medicine is administered by any early years worker.

Table 7.4 First Aid measures

FEBRILE CONVULSIONS

Convulsions (or seizures) are caused by an outburst of electrical activity in the brain. When a baby has an abnormally high fever from an infection, the body temperature rises to the point where the baby's immature temperature regulation mechanism cannot cope. At this critical point, the baby convulses in what appears to be a seizure, or 'fit'.

Signs and symptoms

During convulsions:

▶ The baby's limbs will stiffen and twitch or jerk
▶ The baby will lose consciousness for a few minutes
▶ She may also pass water
▶ The eyes roll back
▶ The baby may dribble

Treatment

▶ **Try not to panic, even though the convulsions can be very frightening.**
▶ **Move potentially harmful objects out of the way.**
▶ **Lay the baby on her side, supported by a cushion or rolled-up blanket, so that her airway is clear.**

DO NOT force anything into your child's mouth – it is not necessary and you may break her teeth. Biting the tongue is rare. The convulsion usually only lasts for a few minutes and afterwards the baby may be drowsy.

▶ **Always call the doctor or ambulance if it is the first time the baby has had a convulsion or if the convulsion lasts for more than five minutes. Sometimes the hopsital will want to carry out further investigations to find out the cause.**

After care

If the baby is hot or you think she has a high temperature, remove most of her clothing and sponge her down with lukewarm water, or you can put her into a lukewarm bath. Give plenty of cool drinks. A dose of paracetamol according to the child's age should also be given if the child has a fever. Use a fan to assist cooling.

BURNS AND SCALDS

Burns are injuries to body tissues caused by heat, chemicals or radiations. Scalds are caused by wet heat, such as steam or hot liquids.

Table 7.4   *(continued)*

Superficial burns involve only the outer layers of the skin, cause redness, swelling, tenderness and usually heal well. Intermediate burns form blisters, can become infected, and need medical aid. Deep burns involve all layers of the skin, which may be pale and charred, may be pain free if the nerves are damaged, and will ALWAYS require medical attention.

Treatment for severe burns and scalds
▶ **Lay the baby down and protect burnt area from ground contact**
▶ **Check ABC of resuscitation and be ready to resuscitate if necessary**
▶ **Gently remove any constricting clothing from the injured area before it begins to swell**
▶ **Cover the injured area loosely with a sterile un-medicated dressing or use a clean non-fluffy tea-towel or pillowcase**

DO NOT remove anything that is sticking to the burn
DO NOT apply lotions, creams or fat to the injury
DO NOT break blisters
DO NOT use plasters
▶ **If the baby is unconscious, lay the baby on her side, supported by a cushion, pillow, rolled-up blanket or something similar**
▶ **Send for medical attention**

Treatment for minor burns and scalds
▶ **Place the injured part under slowly running water, or soak in cold water for 10 minutes**
▶ **Gently remove any constricting articles from the injured area before it begins to swell**
▶ **Dress with clean, sterile, non-fluffy material**

DO NOT use adhesive dressings
DO NOT apply lotions, ointments or fat to burn or scald
DO NOT break blisters or otherwise interfere
▶ **If in doubt, seek medical aid**
Treatment for sunburn
▶ **Remove the baby to the shade and cool the skin by gently sponging the skin with tepid (lukewarm) water**
▶ **Give sips of cold water at frequent intervals**
▶ **If the burns are mild, gently apply an after-sun cream**
▶ **For extensive blistering, seek medical help**

Table 7.4 (continued)

DROWNING

If a baby or small child is discovered under water, either in the bath or a pool, follow these guidelines:

✓ **Call for emergency medical attention. Dial 999**
✓ **Keep child's neck immobilized as you remove him/her from the water.**
✓ **Restore breathing and circulation first.**
✓ **If child is unconscious or you suspect neck injuries, do not bend or turn neck while restoring breathing.**
✓ **Give rescue breathing if the child is not breathing but has a pulse. Breathe forcefully enough to blow air through water in the airway. Do not try to empty water from child's lungs.**
✓ **Do not give up. Give CPR if the child does not have a pulse. Continue until child is revived, until medical help arrives, or until exhaustion stops you.**

Signs and symptoms

Look for one or more of the following:

- unconsciousness; no pulse
- bluish-colored skin
- no visible or audible breath
- pale lips, tongue, and/or nail bed

Immediate treatment

1. **Lie child on flat surface, or begin first aid in the water.**
2. **Check ABCs (Airway, Breathing, Circulation)**
3. **If child is not breathing, open airway and start rescue breathing.**
4. **Check pulse and continue CPR if necessary to restore circulation.**
5. **When breathing and pulse have been restored, treat for shock.**
6. **Have child lie down on his/her side to allow water to drain from the mouth.**
7. **Restore child's body heat by removing wet clothing and covering child with warm blankets.**
8. **Do not give up if breathing and pulse are not restored. Continue CPR until help arrives.**

Activities relating to Chapter 7

ACTIVITY 1

An unwell baby

Imagine you are a nanny looking after a six-month-old baby in his home. When you pick him up from his morning nap, you notice that he is very hot and sweaty; he refuses his bottlefeed and cries fretfully.

*   What would you do first?
*   Prepare a poster display showing the principles of caring for a sick baby.

ACTIVITY 2

Infection and immunisation

Read through the section on common childhood diseases and the information on immunisation.

Prepare a booklet for parents on the childhood diseases for which there is immunisation. Include the following information:

*   the **causes**, **signs** and **symptoms** of the diseases;
*   possible **complications** and **treatment**;
*   the **immunisation schedule**;
*   **contra-indications** to immunisation;

where to go for further advice and help on immunisation.

Make the booklet as eye-catching as possible, using illustrations.

ACTIVITY 3

Health surveillance

Arrange to visit a child health clinic and find out the following information:

*   What surveillance programmes are routinely carried out and by whom?
*   If further tests are necessary, to whom is the child referred?
*   What records are maintained by health visitors?
*   How do health personnel ensure equality of access to health surveillance?

8

Equipment, Toys and Activities

Planning for a baby

Families come under a lot of pressure from friends, from advertising companies and from television programmes to provide the very best clothing and equipment for their new baby. The early years worker is in an important position to be able to advise on the basic principles when choosing equipment. The idealised picture of happy, smiling parents cuddling their precious bundle of joy is hard to resist; advertisers use these images to bombard the new parents with a dazzling array of objects that are deemed 'essential' to happy parenthood. Parents should prioritise their needs by considering all factors relevant to their circumstances:

> ► **Cost**: how much the parents can afford to spend; what may be available on loan from friends who have children past the baby stage? Can some equipment, e.g. the pram, be bought second-hand or hired cheaply?
>
> ► **Lifestyle**: Is the family living in a flat where the lifts are often out of action, in bed and breakfast accommodation, or in a house with a large garden? These factors will affect such decisions as pram vs. combination model or buggy – or where the baby will sleep.
>
> ► **Single or multiple use**: Will the equipment be used for a subsequent baby – in which case the priority may be to buy a large pram on which a toddler can also be seated? It may be worth buying new, quality products if they are to be used again;

> ▶ **Safety and maintenance: D**oes the item of equipment chosen meet all the British Safety Standards? What if it has been bought second-hand? How easy is it to replace worn-out parts?

Clothing and footwear

The layette is the baby's first set of clothes; some shops specialising in baby goods supply complete layettes. There is a vast range of clothing available. Baby clothes should be:

- **loose and comfortable to allow for ease of movement**; as babies grow rapidly, care should be taken that all-in-one stretch suits do not cramp tiny feet – there should always be growing space at the feet to avoid pressure on the soft bones;
- **easy to wash and dry**, as babies need changing often; natural fibres (e.g. cotton and wool mixtures) are more comfortable;
- **non-flammable**: all garments for babies up to three months old must carry a permanent label showing that it has passed the low flammability test for slow burning;
- **easy to put on and take off** – avoid ribbons, bows and lacy-knit fabrics which can trap small fingers and toes;
- **non-irritant** – clothes should be lightweight, soft and warm; some synthetic fibres can be too cold in winter as they do not retain body heat, and too hot in the summer as they do not absorb sweat or allow the skin pores to 'breathe';
- **appropriate for the weather** – e.g. in cooler weather a hat is necessary to prevent the loss of heat from the baby's head; in hot weather, a hat with a wide brim will protect her from the sun.

Note also that:

- several layers of clothing are warmer than one thick garment;
- outside shoes should not be worn until the baby has learned to walk unaided; socks and shoes should be carefully fitted and checked every three months for size;
- babies hate having their faces covered, so choose clothes with front fastenings or with wide envelope necks;
- tights are practical and warm for both boys and girls. Most babies love to kick their way out of socks and woollen bootees;
- clothing needs will vary according to the season, and the baby will need protective clothes such as pram suits, bonnet or sun hat, mittens, bootees.

Figure 8.1   Babies need comfortable clothes, appropriate for the weather

Every parent enjoys dressing a baby up, but there is no need to spend a fortune as babies do grow out of their clothes very quickly.

A BASIC WARDROBE FOR A NEWBORN

- 6 cotton vests (envelope neck or wrap-over style)
- 1 lightweight shawl for swaddling
- 2 pairs of mittens (in winter)
- 2 woollen jackets or cardigans (4 in winter)
- 1 warm winter hat or sun hat with wide brim
- 2 pairs of socks and padders or bootees
- 8 all-in-one stretch suits
- 2 sleepsuits or loose-fitting night-dress
- 1 all-in-one pram suit (quilted/padded)
- nappies, liners, muslin squares, water

CARING FOR A BABY'S CLOTHES

Most shop-bought baby clothes are machine-washable. Woollen garments may benefit from being washed by hand as they can shrink if washed in water that is too hot. A baby's skin is sensitive so the following points should be observed:

- Do not use biological washing powders as these contain strong enzymes.

- Always rinse clothing thoroughly and do not use perfumed fabric conditioners.
- Dry baby clothes and bedclothes in the open air – or a tumble drier if available – as they will retain their softness.

A label sewn in to each garment provides instructions about washing, bleaching, dry-cleaning and ironing.

Equipment for a young baby

Babies will need somewhere:

- to sleep
- to feed
- to play

- to be bathed
- to sit
- to be transported

Equipment for sleeping

Cradles and **'Moses baskets'** (wicker baskets with carrying handles) can be used as a bed for a young baby, but are unsuitable for transporting the baby outside or in a car.

Prams and carrycots come in a wide variety of designs; **safety mattresses** are available which are ventilated at the head section to prevent the risk of suffocation. Prams can be bought second-hand or hired for the first year of a baby's life; they must meet the following safety requirements:

> ▶ brakes should be efficient and tested regularly;
> ▶ a shopping basket should be positioned underneath to prevent shopping bags being hung on the handles and causing over-balancing;
> ▶ have anchor points for a safety harness;
> ▶ be stable, easy to steer and the right height for the carer to be able to push easily without stooping.
> ▶ the mattress must be firm enough to support the baby's back.

Cots

Often a baby will move into a cot for sleeping when he has outgrown his carrycot, but they are suitable for newborn babies. Cots usually have slatted sides, which allow the baby to see out with one side able to be lowered and secured by safety catches. Safety requirements are:

> ▶ bars must be no more than 7 cm apart;
> ▶ safety catches must be child-proof;
> ▶ the mattress should fit snugly with no gaps;
> ▶ cot bumpers (foam padded screens tied at the head end of the cot)
>   are not recommended;
> ▶ if it has been painted, check that lead-free paint has been used.

Figure 8.2   Moses basket with patterned cards

TRAVEL COT

This is a folding cot with fabric sides, suitable for temporary use only; it is especially useful if the family travels away from home a lot and can double as a playpen when the mattress is removed.

BLANKETS AND SHEETS

These should be easy to wash and dry as they will need frequent laundering; the ideal fabric for sheets is brushed cotton and blankets are often made from cellular acrylic fabric, which is both lightweight, warm and easily washable.

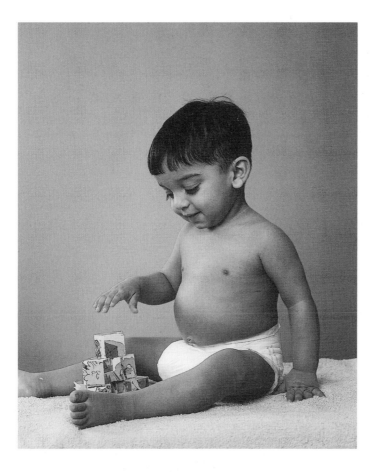

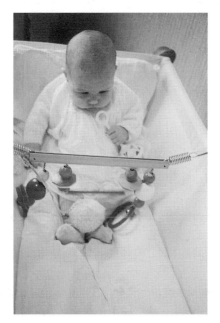

Figure 8.3   (a) Playing with bricks (b) Playing with cradle gym

A small baby can be bathed in a plastic baby bath with a non-slip surface. A purpose-designed baby bath is easily transportable (when empty) and may be used in the following ways:

- on a table or worktop, ideally at about hip height to prevent excessive bending;
- on the fixed base bought for a carrycot;
- on a stand provided with the bath; within the adult bath.

After a few months, the baby can be bathed in the adult bath, but carers should:

- guard against back strain;
- always cover hot taps because of the risk of burns;
- always use a non-slip rubber mat in the bath;
- check that the temperature of the bathroom is warm enough.

> **Safety note: Never leave a baby alone in any bath, even for a few seconds**

Babies will also need their own towels and toiletries.

Equipment for feeding

If the baby is being bottlefed, 8 to 10 bottles and teats, sterilising equipment and formula milk will be required. If she is being breastfed, one bottle and teat is useful to provide extra water or fruit juice. The baby's mother may also require breast pads and special support bras.

There are many different chairs available, ranging from rigid reclining low-chairs to full size high-chairs which are useful for the older baby

Equipment for sitting

BOUNCING CRADLE

This is a soft fabric seat, which can be used from birth to about six months. Babies and their carers generally appreciate it as it is easily transported from room to room, encouraging the baby's full involvement in everyday activities. It should **always** be placed on the floor – **never** on a worktop or bed as even very young babies can 'bounce' themselves off.

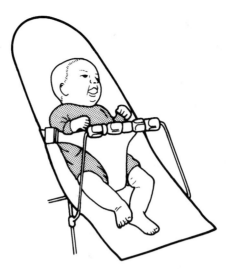

Figure 8.4   Bouncing cradle

RIGID RECLINING ADJUSTABLE LOW CHAIR

These are usually car seats that may be detached from the car and used as indoor seats for young babies (see car seats below).

HIGH CHAIR

A high chair may be used for a baby who is able to sit unaided. It should always be used with a safety harness, preferably a fitted harness. The high chair should:

> ▶ be designed for easy cleaning, i.e. no ledges and corners for trapping dirt;
> ▶ conform to the safety standard BS 5799;
> ▶ include a large, firmly fixed tray.

SAFETY HARNESS

A harness should always be used to strap the baby into her pram, pushchair or high chair to prevent her falling out. It should have straps for the shoulders as well as the waist and crotch, and conform to BS 6684.

The importance of play

Play is central to a child's learning. It helps children to use what they know and to understand things about the world and the people they meet.

From a very early age babies learn best:

• by doing;
• by seeing; and
• by touching.

They perceive very little difference between work and play. Play is open-ended; even when there is a goal in sight, such as building a tower of blocks, the **process** is more important than the product. Often play is under-valued by adults as taking second place to other aspects of family life. However, if play is to provide the wide range of opportunities for learning, then adult involvement is essential (see page 62 on Bruner).

Equipment for playing

Babies like to be held where they can see human faces, especially the carer's face, clearly; they prefer toys which are brightly coloured and which make a noise.

The following chart suggests toys and playthings appropriate for babies at different stages of development; it also provides a rationale for choice of plaything.

SAFETY OF TOYS AND PLAYTHINGS

Babies have no concept of danger, so it is important to supervise their environment for safety. Whether buying or making toys for babies, the following safety points should be considered:

✓ Materials should be durable, to avoid accidents from broken or splintered edges.
✓ Any painted items must use non-toxic paint.
✓ Toys should not contain small parts that can come loose and be swallowed.
✓ Strings should never be used to attach anything around the baby's neck.
✓ Be careful with heavy objects that a baby could injure herself with.
✓ Check soft toys – e.g. teddies and rag dolls – for safety; try to pull the eyes out of a 'teddy' or remove small parts which a baby could choke on or put in her nose or ears.
✓ Always try to buy goods displaying the appropriate safety symbol (see Figure 8.7).

Table 8.1 Toys and playthings

Age of baby	Plaything or toy	Rationale
In the first six months provide:	A mobile: this should be placed within her field of vision, about 20 cm from her face	Promotes visual and perceptual development and enables the baby to explore the world around her
	High-contrast black and white patterns on cards securely attached to the inside of her pram or cot	Promotes visual development; babies find black and white patterns and bright contrasting colours fascinating
	Musical toys, chiming ball and rattles	Promotes auditory development; babies learn that they can control their own environment by their own actions
	Soft balls and cubes	Promotes sense of touch and develops an awareness of how objects can be distinguished by feel
	Bath toys – plastic ducks, cups etc.	Promotes love of water for happy bath times, sensory development and learning about floating, sinking, pouring
	Activity mat, including reflective surfaces and musical features	Promotes hand-eye co-ordination, manipulative skills and dexterity; also stimulates interest and the feeling of controlling the environment
	Stacking beakers, building bricks (to stack, to knock down)	Promotes manipulative skills and a sense of achievement
From six months to one year also provide:	Rag books	Emotional needs are met through the close contact when reading 'with' a young baby; books that are safe and fun for the baby to handle serve as a good introduction to the world of reading
	Saucepans and spoons	Promotes motor skill development and sensory development; also promotes emotional development and the sense of being able to shape and control the baby's own environment
	An empty cardboard box (makes an exciting tunnel for a baby to crawl through)	Promotes perceptual development – a baby learns that the world stays the same even when she cannot see it; also builds up her sense of security and confidence
From one year to eighteen months, also provide:	Short, fat non-toxic crayons and cheap drawing paper	Promotes sensory development, fine manipulative skills, hand-eye co-ordination; also encourages imagination and creativity
	Powder paints, mixed thickly, and a stubby paint brush **Once the baby can walk confidently**, also provide: toys for pushing and pulling; this can be bought or home-made (see Activity at end of chapter)	Promotes motor skills, in particular balance and co-ordination; helps to develop cognitive processes – solving problems when a pull-along toy becomes trapped, and builds up the baby's confidence and sense of being in control

Figure 8.5   Playing at home

SAFETY SYMBOLS

> ▶ **The kite mark**: this mark on any product means that the British Standards Institution has checked the manufacturer's claim that their product meets the specific standards.
> ▶ **The safety mark**: the safety mark means that a product has been checked to ensure that it meets the British Standards Institution for safety only.
> ▶ **The lion mark**: this symbol is only found on British-made toys and means that they have met the safety standards required.
> ▶ **The CE mark**: this symbol means that products comply with European and British safety standards.

NB: Toys and games bought from market stalls or cheap foreign imports may be copies of well-known brand-name toys but may not meet the safety standards.

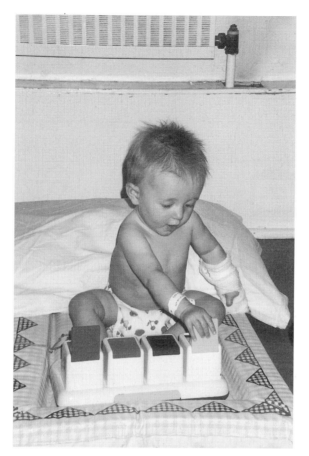

Figure 8.6 Playing in hospital

Equipment for transport

BABY SLINGS

Baby slings, used on the front of the carer's body enable close physical contact between carer and baby, but can cause back strain if used with heavy babies. Using a baby sling makes the baby feel secure and it leaves your arms free; they can usually be used with the baby facing outwards or inwards. Follow these guidelines when using a baby sling:

- Ask someone to help you the first time you lift the baby into the sling.
- Make sure the sling has a good head support for the baby.
- never try to adjust holding clips when the baby is in the sling.
- always protect the baby's head when you lean forward

Child 'back carriers' which fit on a frame like a rucksack are suitable for larger babies when out walking; make sure that she is comfortable and that the leg openings do not restrict her.

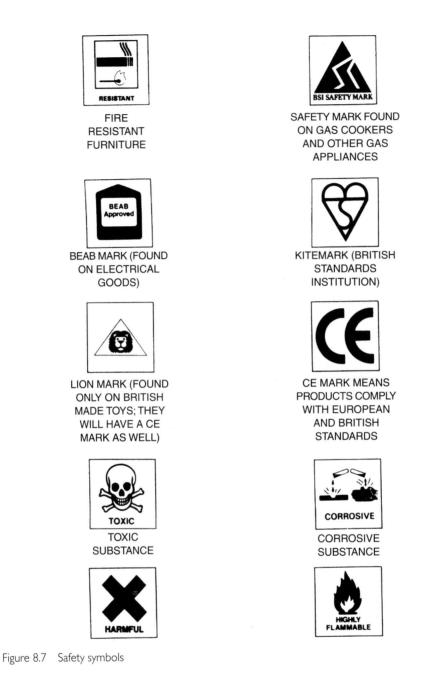

Figure 8.7   Safety symbols

Safety in the car

When travelling in a car, the baby's safety is of paramount importance. The law states that all children under the age of three must use an appropriate restraint when travelling in the front seat of the car. Child safety seats must not be placed in a passenger seat equipped with an airbag. An appropriate

Figure 8.8   Baby in front sling

restraint is one that is suitable for the child's weight and size and which can be correctly fitted into the car. It is the *weight* not the age of the baby that determines which seat is most suitable and will afford maximum security. (Car seats should meet the European safety standard ECE R44 03.)

NB: Adult seatbelts are never appropriate for babies.

Points to remember when travelling with a baby in a car:

- Never be tempted to travel with the baby in your lap – you wouldn't be able to hold on to her in an accident and the weight of your body could injure her on impact;
- Small babies can be transported in a sturdy carrycot with fixed straps on the back seat or in a rearward facing baby car seat (see Figure 8.9); for babies under 10 kg, these seats can be used also as a first seat in the home.

- Keep the baby in the rearward facing position until she's 9 months old or until she weighs at least 10 kg (22 lb).
- Never buy a second hand car seat; after any car accident, replace your seat belts, the child's car seat and the anchorage straps as they will have been subject to strain and may be ineffective.
- Try the car seat out in your car before buying.
- Always follow the instructions carefully before buying.

Any kind of outing with a baby requires careful planning and preparation:

✓ Try to travel when the roads are empty if possible.
✓ Carry a window blind to block bright sunlight from the baby's face.
✓ Take all the necessary equipment for changing and feeding for the whole journey.
✓ Don't forget soothing music on tapes and some toys to keep her amused.

Prams, pushchairs or combination models

For the first three months, a baby must be able to lie flat and will need either:

- a traditional pram or carry-cot pram,
- a pushchair, or
- a combination model.

Figure 8.9   Baby in rearward-facing car seat

PRAMS AND CARRY-COT PRAMS

These may be new or second-hand, but should have the following safety features:

✔ stability: they should not tip over easily;
✔ efficient brakes;
✔ should be efficient
✔ be the right height for the parent or carer to push easily without stooping;
✔ have anchor points for a safety harness

PUSHCHAIRS

Pushchairs should not be used for long periods of sleeping or when the baby is under 6 months.

Pushchairs:

* must have safety locks to prevent the frame from collapsing when in use;
* are lighter and easier to manoeuvre than prams;
* are easy to store;
* are suitable for use on public transport, and
* may be fitted with optional extras such as hoods, aprons, parasols and shopping baskets;
* must have anchor points for the baby's safety harness.

COMBINATION MODELS

Combination models are a compromise between a pram and a pushchair. They have a wide range of features that enable parents to choose one to suit their own needs:

* a reclining tilting seat that can be used from birth and for as long as the baby needs a pushchair;
* choice of positions so that the baby may face outwards or inwards;
* a wide range of accessories.

Safety points with prams and pushchairs

✔ Always strap a baby into her pram once she is able to sit up.
✔ Make sure that the baby is properly strapped into her pushchair, with a 5-point harness.
✔ Always put the brake on the pram or pushchair when you have stopped.
✔ Remember to check the pram or pushchair regularly for any loose screws.
✔ Never hang shopping from the handles of a pushchair, as it could tip over.

HARNESS AND REINS

A walking rein attached to a harness gives a toddler freedom of movement whilst being safely in an adult's control.

Other useful equipment

SAFETY GATES

Constructed from metal bars or softly padded mesh fabric, safety gates may be adjusted to fit any stairway or doorway. Parents and carers can be confident that a baby is prevented from wandering into more dangerous parts of the house.

NIGHT LIGHTS

Night lights can be very reassuring to a baby, and also enable parents or carers to check on the baby without disturbing her. They are available as plugs, which fit in any mains electrical socket in the nursery, or as cordless, battery operated units which can be attached to the baby's cot.

SMOKE ALARMS

Every home should have a smoke alarm which emits a piercing sound when activated by smoke. Smoke alarms should regularly be tested manually and most models incorporate a low battery warning.

LOCKS AND LATCHES

Locks can be bought to fix to any cupboard, drawer or kitchen appliance. These are useful for securing the contents of cupboards containing sharp implements or chemical cleaners.

Safety and prevention of accidents

Babies are vulnerable to accidents because they have no awareness of danger and cannot control their environment; they are totally dependent on their parents or carers to make their world safe.

PREVENTION OF ACCIDENTS

Parents and child carers can reduce the risks of accidents to babies by the following means:

* be a good role model – set a safe example;
* make the home, garden and nursery as accident-proof as possible;
* never leave a baby alone in the house;
* always try to buy goods displaying the appropriate safety symbol.

PREVENTING ACCIDENTS IN THE HOME

Accidents are the single largest cause of death of babies over one year. During the first 18 months of life, babies are unable to understand the idea of danger. Babies are totally dependent on caring adults to keep their environment safe and happy. It is impossible to make any house baby-proof in terms of accidents, but it is worth going to each room in turn and remedying any possible dangerous situation. The most important aspect of preventing accidents is never to leave the baby alone unless you are sure that she is safe and secure, e.g. in her cot or strapped in her pram within sight.

Choking and suffocation

Choking and suffocation is the largest cause of accidental death in babies under one year; and older children are also at risk when playing on their own or eating unsupervised:

- **DO NOT** use a pillow for babies under one year old. Baby nests must meet British Standards No. 6595 and have a flat head area. Baby nests should only be used for carrying a baby – never for leaving a sleeping baby unattended.
- **DO NOT** leave rattles, teething rings or squeeze toys in the baby's cot; they can become wedged in the baby's mouth and cause suffocation.
- **DO NOT** leave a baby alone with a propped-up bottle – always hold the baby whilst feeding.
- **DO NOT** let a baby get hold of tiny items like coins, marbles, dried peas, buttons or Lego; babies explore with their mouths and can easily choke on small objects.
- **DO NOT** leave babies alone with finger foods such as bananas, carrots, cheese etc. Always supervise eating and drinking.
- **DO NOT** give peanuts to children under four years because they can easily choke on them or inhale them into their lungs, causing infection and lung damage.
- **DO** use a firm mattress that meets British Standard No. 1877. For babies over one year old, use a pillow that meets the same standard for allowing air to pass through freely whatever position the baby is in.
- **DO** check that there are no hanging cords – for example from a window blind – which could catch around a child's neck and strangle them if they fall.
- **DO** keep all plastic bags away from babies and children and teach older children never to put plastic bags on their heads
- **DO** be aware that dummies on long ribbons and cardigans with ribbons around the necks can pull tight around a baby's neck if caught

on a hook or knob. A dummy must meet safety standards with holes in the flange, in case it is drawn in to the back of the throat.

- **DO** check that any toys given to babies are safe, with no small loose parts or jagged edges.
- **DO** supervise a baby playing with paper, as she may bite off small pieces and choke on them.

Burns and scalds

As children learn to crawl, climb and walk, the risk of scalds or burns increases.

- **DO NOT** use gas or paraffin heaters in children's bedrooms.
- **DO NOT** let the baby play at your feet while you are cooking.
- **DO NOT** leave burning cigarettes in ashtrays.
- **DO NOT** leave a boiling pot unattended on the stove.
- **DO NOT** use tablecloths which babies can pull down on top of themselves.
- **DO NOT** ever leave a baby alone in a bath, even for a few moments.
- **DO NOT** leave a hose lying in the sun; water in it can get hot enough to scald a baby.
- **DO** keep the water temperature for the house set at about 140°F/60°C, to prevent scalds and burns.
- **DO** protect fires with a fixed fine-mesh fire guard. Note: It is illegal to leave a child under 12 in a room with an open fire.
- **DO** keep matches and lighters well out of reach.
- **DO** choose night-clothes and dressing gowns that are flame resistant (BS 3121).
- **DO** install automatic smoke alarms.
- **DO** use fire doors in nurseries and schools; and check you know the location of fire extinguishers and fire blankets.
- **DO** keep a baby away from the area while you are cooking; always turn pan handles inwards; cooker guards are not a good idea as they can get very hot.
- **DO** keep kettles and hot drinks well out of reach; use a coiled kettle flex and never pass hot drinks over the heads of babies.
- **DO** test bath water before putting a baby in. Always put cold water in first and then add the hot water. A special plastic strip thermometer can be stuck to the inside of the bath to check the temperature.

Falls

All babies fall once they are walking, but there are ways of ensuring that they do not fall too far or too hard:

- **DO NOT** use baby-walkers. Child safety experts agree that these are dangerous and cause many accidents as babies steer themselves *into* dangerous situations.
- **DO NOT** leave babies unattended on a table, work surface, bed or sofa; lie them on the floor instead.
- **DO NOT** place furniture under windows where babies may be tempted to climb.
- **DO** use stairgates at the top and the bottom of the stairs and at doors, which might be left open. (BS 4125).
- **DO** fit vertical bars to dangerous windows (Note: horizontal bars encourage climbing).
- **DO** fit child-proof window safety catches on all windows.
- **DO** use a harness (BS 6684) in the highchair, pram, pushchair or supermarket trolley.
- **DO** teach babies how to use the stairs safely; teach them to come down stairs backwards on all fours.
- **DO** install window guards or adjust them so that they cannot open more than 10 cm.
- **DO** clean up spills immediately to prevent slips and falls.

Poisoning

The peak age for accidents with poisons is one to three years old, when children are highly mobile and inquisitive.

- **DO NOT** transfer chemicals e.g. weedkiller into other containers such as a lemonade bottle as a child will not know the difference until it is too late.
- **DO NOT** store dangerous household chemicals e.g. bleach, disinfectant, white spirit etc. in the cupboard under the sink. Use a safer, locked cupboard instead.
- **DO** keep all medicines in a locked cupboard.
- **DO** use child-proof containers and ensure that they are closed properly.
- **DO** teach children not to eat berries or fungi in the garden or in the park.
- **DO** keep rubbish and kitchen waste in a tightly covered container, or better still, behind a securely locked door.
- **DO** store children's vitamins in a safe place. Poisoning by an overdose of vitamins is very common.

Cuts

Glass presents the biggest safety hazard to babies and young children; every year, about 7000 children end up in hospital after being cut by glass.

- **DO** use special safety glass in doors; this is relatively harmless if it does break, whereas ordinary glass breaks into lethal, jagged pieces.
- **DO** mark large picture windows with coloured strips or decals to make it obvious when they are closed.
- **DO** use plastic drinking cups and bottles.
- **DO** keep all knives, scissors and razors out of reach.
- **DO** teach children never to run with a pencil or lolly stick in their mouth.
- **DO** teach children never to play with doors; if possible fit a device to the top of doors to prevent them from slamming and pinching fingers.

Drowning

A baby or toddler can drown in a very shallow amount of water – even a bucket with a few inches of water in it presents a risk.

- **DO NOT** ever leave a child alone in the bath.
- **DO NOT** leave an older child looking after a baby or toddler in the bath.
- **DO** use a non-slip mat in the bath.
- **DO** always supervise water play.
- **DO** guard ponds, water butts and ditches.
- **DO** keep the toilet lid down at all times or fit locking device; toddlers are fascinated by the swirling water action and can fall in and drown.

Electric shocks

Babies and toddlers may suffer electric shock from poking small objects into sockets or from playing with electric plugs.

- **DO** fit safety dummy plugs or socket covers to all electric sockets.
- **DO** check that the plugs are correctly wired and safe; when buying Christmas tree lights; check for the British Standard No. 4647.

Games and activities for babies

Table 8.2 Activities and games

Age or stage of development	Activity or game and description	Comments
From birth to three months	**Display and play:** make a collection of items from everyday life, e.g. food packets, coloured thread, brightly coloured postcards, rattles and squeezy toys which make a noise. Hold the object about 12 ins from her face and watch her facial expression as she registers the object's appearance	Promotes visual and perceptual development. At this stage, babies prefer to look at human faces and at boldly, defined patterns.
From two to five months	**Bubble show:** prop the baby up in a bouncing cradle or against some cushions on the floor and prepare a bubble lotion and a metal or plastic ring to blow through. Blow the bubbles across and above the baby and watch her track the movements	Promotes visual and perceptual development. Babies learn how to follow a moving object with their eyes.
From two months onwards	**Peek-a-boo:** sit close in front of the baby and cover your face with your hands. Then open your hands, smile and say 'BOO'.	Promotes the development of understanding of **object permanence**. Also promotes social development and waiting to take turn.
From eight months onwards	**Finger-play:** there are a great many rhymes to be used with your fingers; one example is: Round and round the garden like a teddy bear (swirl your index finger around plam of the baby's hand) One step, Two steps (walk fingers up baby's arm) Tickly under there! (tickle under baby's underarm)	Promotes visual and auditory development; also introduces the baby to simple number counting games.
From nine months onwards	**Knee-bouncing rhymes:** some babies are easily frightened by sudden dropping movements, so be gentle with a young baby; one example is: Horsey, horsey don't you stop, Just let your feet go clippety-clop, Your tail goes swish and the wheels go round, Giddy-up, we're homeward bound.	Helps language development and an appreciation of music, rhyme and movement

Table 8.2   *Activities and games (continued)*

Age or stage of development	Activity or game and description	Comments
From one year onwards	**Matching game:** assemble a small collection of plastic farm animals. Select a cow and ask the baby: 'Find me a cow like this one'. Help her if necessary and then repeat for all the other animals.	Promotes the skill of classifying and sorting objects; also promotes language development as she names objects.
	Finger puppets: make some finger puppets. Small faces can be drawn on paper and then taped to form a cap that fits over the fingertip; or you can make them from felt with face and hair stuck on. Make one small puppet for the baby and two larger ones for yourself. Try a simple rhyme with finger movements, such as 'My little man bows down . . .'	Develops social, communication and imaginative skills; also develops fine manipulative skills, through the finger control

Activities relating to Chapter 8

ACTIVITY I

Clothes for a baby

You have been asked to advise on the purchase of a layette for a newborn baby.

- Make a list of the items you consider to be essential, excluding nappies and waterproof pants.
- Visit several shops and find out the cost of all the items in your list.

Evaluate your selection, by checking:

- the ease of washing and drying;
- the design and colours used – are you reinforcing the stereotypes of pink for girls or blue for boys?;
- the safety aspects – no fancy bows and ties etc.;
- the suitability of the fabrics used;
- the quantity of clothes needed;
- the final cost of the layette.

ACTIVITY 2

Toys for babies

Visit a toyshop and look at the range of toys for babies under eighteen months old. List the toys and activities under two headings:

1   toys that strengthen muscles and improve co-ordination-ordination;
2   toys that will particularly stimulate the senses of touch and sight.

What safety symbols are shown on the toys?

If you were asked to suggest toys and activities for a baby with visual impairment, what specific toys could you suggest?

ACTIVITY 3

A treasure chest

Make a treasure chest for a baby aged between eight and eighteen months. The baby should be able to sit comfortably without any support.

1   Use a strong, shallow cardboard box, an old solid wooden drawer or a wicker shopping-basket. Check that there are no staples, splinters or jagged edges.
2   Select a variety of interesting objects – about 10 to 15 in all – which will stimulate each of the baby's senses: i.e. different shapes, weights, colours and textures. You may also be able to include objects that have a distinctive smell, e.g. a small empty perfume bottle or a lavender bag.
3   Sit to one side and observe the baby playing by herself with the contents of the drawer. Write a detailed timed observation of the activity, including the following points:

    • what the baby does with each object;
    • how long she plays with each object;
    • what expressions or noises she makes;
    • how involved she is in the activity.

4   Evaluate the activity in terms of its value to the baby's overall development and enjoyment. What would you change if you were to repeat the exercise?

ACTIVITY 4

Accidents in the home and garden

Read through the section on prevention of accidents, pages 180–184. Draw up a chart with the following headings: kitchen; living room; bathroom; bedroom; stairs; garden etc. In each column or row, state the possible dangers and what you could do to make each room safer for a baby who has just begun to walk and to climb up on furniture.

ACTIVITY 5

Accidents in the workplace

In practical work placement, research the following information:

TASK ONE: FIRE AND SAFETY

1 What are the instructions in the event of a fire?
2 The location of the fire extinguishers?
3 The location of the fire exits?

TASK TWO: ACCIDENT REPORT BOOK

Every workplace is required to maintain a record of accidents. Ask permission to look at the book at your placement.

1 Present the information in the accident book in the form of a pie chart, using the following categories of accident: falls, cuts, burns and scalds, choking, stings etc.
2 For each category of accident, state how it could have been prevented and what treatment should be given.

NB: Remember to preserve confidentiality – do not use names

9

A Guide to Working with Babies

Contents

Qualities of a good early years worker   Working as a nanny in someone else's home   Caring for babies outside the family home   Caring for babies with special needs   The needs of parents and carers   Contracts and legislation relating to caring for babies

A career guide to working with babies

The majority of babies under eighteen months are cared for by their parents, in their own homes. According to the most recent General Household Survey, 64% of all mothers who work full-time or part-time outside the house use one or several types of child care: 38% use childminders or nannies; 36% use families and friends; 11% use private nurseries and 2% use private preparatory nursery schools.

What qualities make a good early years worker?

Above all else, an early years worker needs to like babies and children and to enjoy being with them. Caring as a quality is largely invisible, difficult to quantify and more noticeable when absent than when present. The main individual characteristics are:

✓ **Listening**: attentive listening is a vital part of the caring relationship. Sometimes a child's real needs are communicated more by what is left unsaid than what is actually spoken. Facial expressions, posture, and other forms of body language all give clues to a child's feelings. A good carer will be aware of these forms of non-verbal communication.

✓ **Comforting**: this has a physical and emotional meaning. Physical comfort may be provided by a cuddle at a time of anxiety, or a social worker may provide a reassuring safe environment to a distressed child. Touching, listening and talking can all provide emotional comfort as well.

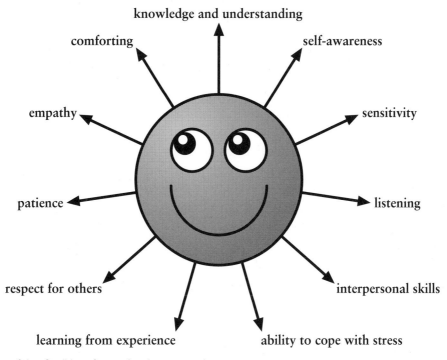

knowledge and understanding

comforting

self-awareness

empathy

sensitivity

patience

listening

respect for others

interpersonal skills

learning from experience

ability to cope with stress

Figure 9.1   Qualities of a good early years worker

✓ **Empathy**: this should not be confused with sympathy. Some people find it easy to appreciate how someone else is feeling by imagining themselves in that person's position. A good way of imagining how a strange environment appears to a young child is to kneel on the floor and try to view it from a child's perspective.

✓ **Sensitivity**: the ability to be aware of and responsive to the feelings and needs of another person. Being sensitive to others' needs requires the carer to anticipate their feelings, e.g. a child whose mother has been admitted to hospital, or whose pet dog has just died.

✓ **Patience**: being patient and tolerant of other people's methods of dealing with problems even when the carer feels that his or her own way is better; e.g. letting a child develop independence by dressing himself even when you need to hurry.

✓ **Respect**: a carer should have an awareness of a child's personal rights, dignity and privacy – and must show this at all times; every child is unique and so the carer's approach will need to be tailored to each individual's needs.

✓ **Interpersonal skills**: a caring relationship is a two-way process. One does not have to *like* the child one is caring for but warmth and friendliness help to create a positive atmosphere and to break down barriers. Acceptance is important; the carer should always look beyond the disability or disruptive behaviour to recognise and accept the person.

✓ **Self-awareness**: a carer can be more effective if able to perceive what effect his or her behaviour has on other people; being part of a team enables us to discover how others perceive us and to modify our behaviour in the caring relationship accordingly.

✓ **Coping with stress**: caring for others effectively in a full-time capacity requires energy and it is important to be aware of the possibility of professional burn-out. In order to help others we must first help ourselves; the carer who never relaxes or develops any outside interests is more likely to suffer 'burn-out' than the carer who finds his own time and space.

✓ **Knowledge and understanding**: an understanding of the needs of the child and of the broad stages of development through which children pass; such knowledge and understanding enables the early years worker to encourage children's all-round development.

✓ **Learning from experience**: it is important to continue to learn and grow as professionals; observing babies and children enable the worker to avoid making assumptions about a child and helps to identify any special need a child may have.

Working with babies

There are many opportunities for employment for people with child care qualifications to work with babies, for example in:

* the family home, as a nanny;
* local authority day nurseries;
* maternity units in hospitals;
* private nurseries;
* workplace crêches;
* babysitting;
* child-minding; and
* jobs within the holiday and leisure industry – e.g. abroad as a ski or summer resort nanny or as a nanny in a special children's hotel.

Working as a nanny

A nanny is someone who is making a career out of caring for children. Responsibilities vary widely from post to post, as illustrated by a selection of advertisements for nannies.

London: Immediate start Qualified and experienced Nanny/maternity nurse. Must have baby experience, multiples a bonus. To assist in the care of triplets – 2 boys and one girl now 4 months old. Must be dedicated and reliable in these exceptional circumstances of a lone father. Salary and hours neg.

Nottingham: High powered family require live-in or daily nanny for boy 16 months and newborn expected very soon. Nursery duties, sole charge after a few months. Good baby experience reqd. Own bedroom, en-suite in beautiful new house. Good salary.

Hull: fantastic informal family seek bright and bubbly live-in or daily nanny for twin boys 8 months. Own super nanny suite, driver preferred. Spend holidays in Aspen and the south coast. Good salary.

Surrey: prestigious family URGENTLY require residential nanny to care for boys 6 and 8 and baby expected in Nov. Nursery duties only 7–6.30.
House staff kept (butler, chef, chauffeur, housekeeper etc.) must be able to spend Summer on the Greek islands with them. Tennis courts and swimming pool on the estate. Accommodation in cottage in the garden. Call to arrange interview.

Aberdeenshire: Daily Job. Care of baby and toddler. Very high salary. No babysitting! Evenings and w/e's off. Please call now.

Figure 9.2   Selection of ads for nannies

Most jobs involve the nanny having full responsibility for all aspects of childcare, including:

- the children's health and welfare while they are under your supervision;
- their social, emotional and educational development while caring for them as their nanny;
- ensuring that the children always play in safety in an environment free from danger and minor hazards;
- some light domestic duties, closely related to the care of the children.

Some employers place greater emphasis on experience and personality than on professional qualifications. Other parents will only employ someone with a recognised childcare qualification.

There are many nanny employment agencies which usually offer qualified nannies:

> - contact with a wide range of suitable employers within your chosen area of work;
> - advice on matters of pay, tax and contractual obligations, such as hours of pay and specific duties;
> - a formal contract between a nanny and the employer (see page 211);
> - a free follow-up service after the start of employment, with the aim of sorting out any teething problems that may arise.

The interview

Nanny agencies offer advice to parents on what to ask at interview to ensure that the person they employ suits their particular family's needs. Typical questions include:

1. WHY DO YOU WISH TO BE A NANNY?

Employers are looking for someone whose answers show a love of children. Taking care of children involves a very big commitment and is not a suitable career for anyone who is not enthusiastic or who is unsure about being a nanny.

2. WHAT ARE YOUR CHILDCARE EXPERIENCES?

You should be prepared to give a brief account of your past jobs, your formal college training and other relevant experience, such as regular baby-sitting jobs, playgroup experience etc. Most employers will also ask for at least three references from people who can verify your experience and your suitability for childcare work.

3. WHAT ARE YOUR CHILD-REARING PHILOSOPHIES?

Employers may ask how you would react in a specific situation; for example, if a child refuses to put on his coat when you need to take her to nursery school and 'throws a tantrum'. Always answer truthfully and try to expand on how you feel about dealing with difficult behaviour and any experiences and examples you can relate.

4. WHY DOES THIS PARTICULAR POST INTEREST YOU?

You should already be aware of the details of the post or job specification, i.e. the hours, responsibilities, days off, salary etc. The employer will want to know if there is any particular reason why you have chosen the post; this might be the ages of the children or it might be the location.

5. WHAT DO YOU FEEL ARE YOUR PERSONAL QUALITIES THAT SUIT YOU FOR THIS JOB?

Many nannies feel uncomfortable when asked to list their personal strengths; they feel that they are boasting. However, an employer may have several candidates to interview and will need to know where you feel your special qualities lie, so try to speak honestly without being embarrassed.

6. WHAT DOMESTIC DUTIES WOULD YOU EXPECT TO BE INCLUDED IN THE JOB?

This area of work is one that is most often the subject of disagreement between a nanny and the family. Some nannies are willing to do all the family's ironing in addition to caring for the children's laundry; others may resent being asked to do any tasks that are not directly related to care of the children. Issues such as extra baby-sitting duties in the evenings also need to be discussed.

7. WHAT ARE YOUR HOBBIES AND INTERESTS?

Most employers are trying to find out what sort of person you are, to see whether or not you will fit in with the family. For instance, some families will be looking for a nanny that wants to travel, or one who will encourage children's sporting interests.

Other typical questions if you are applying for a live-in nanny post are:

1. WHAT QUALITIES ARE YOU LOOKING FOR IN A FAMILY?

It is very important to you and to the family that the 'chemistry' is right. Employers want a nanny whose personality meshes with their own. Some

Figure 9.3   An interview

live-in nannies expect to be part of the family, while others view the relationship as strictly that of employer/employee. Ask relevant questions if they are not answered already, e.g.: Are you expected to eat with the family, and will you be expected to travel on holidays with the family?

2. Can you drive?

If you drive you will be asked if you have a clean driving licence. You may need to find out whether there is a car available for your day off and what your duties are in respect of driving the children to school etc.

3. Do you smoke?

The employer will probably describe the house rules about smoking. You should know if any members of the household smoke and exactly what the rules are concerning smoking in your time off in the house.

4. Do you have any special dietary needs or any medical problems?

If you have any allergies or special dietary needs or preferences, you should mention them at the interview. Some employers ask for a letter from your G.P.

Preparation for the interview

First impressions are very important. Dress smartly and avoid lots of make-up and jewellery. Non-verbal communication is also important:

- **facial expression**: you may be very nervous, but make an effort to smile and to appear cheerful and relaxed;
- try to maintain **eye-contact** when the interviewer is speaking to you and when you reply;
- **shake hands firmly** with the interviewer, and try not to fidget; clasp your hands loosely in your lap; never sit with your arms folded;
- **eat before the interview**, so that your stomach does not rumble;
- **don't smoke** even if the interviewer does – it is not acceptable to smoke during your working hours even if the household has no objections;
- **be realistic**: there may be many other applicants for the post; if you are not successful it does not reflect on you personally.

Caring for babies outside the family home

Local Authority Day Nurseries

Local Authority day nurseries are funded by social services and offer full-time provision for children under school age. They are particularly important in working with families, who may be facing many challenges. Staffing levels are high, the usual ratio being one staff member for every four children. Some local authority day nurseries also operate as **family centres**, providing advice, guidance and counselling to the families with difficulties. They usually have a staff of trained nursery nurses and sometimes trained teachers or social workers will work on the staff. Most day nurseries operate a system of **key workers**.

Key workers

A key worker is usually a trained early years worker who takes on responsibility for one or more particular babies each day. By ensuring continuity of care, the difficulty of separation for the baby from her parent is minimised. Parents appreciate having a familiar worker with whom they can talk in confidence about any concerns they may have relating to their baby's wellbeing. Responsibilities of a key worker will include:

- assessing the baby's needs, often by visiting the family before admission to the nursery;
- sharing information with the parents on all aspects of their baby's care;
- planning the baby's daily routine;
- meeting all the baby's needs when in the nursery, involving:
  - physical needs: nappy changing, skin care and bottle feeding;
  - emotional needs: settling the baby on arrival each session and comforting her when distressed;
  - intellectual needs: planning a learning programme to promote development and to stimulate the baby;
  - observing and recording the baby's development;
  - returning the baby to the care of her parents at the end of each session with a report.

Private day nurseries and workplace crèches

The increase in numbers of working mothers has led to the setting up of more private day nurseries and workplace crèches which care for babies and pre-school children during the normal working week. Such organisations are required by law to register with social services and are subject to regular inspections of facilities, safety and staff.

Childminding

Childminders usually use their own home to care for babies and pre-school children. Similar registration and inspection duties apply to child-minding as to day care. The local authority must:

- specify the maximum number of children;
- require the premises and equipment used to be adequately maintained and kept safe;
- require a record to be kept of the name and address of:
  - any child looked after,
  - any person who assists in looking after such a child, and
  - any person living or likely to be living on those premises;
- require that they be notified by the child-minder, in writing, of any change in the circumstances above.

Child-minders are allowed to fix their own charges and many nursery nurses choose this career option when they have children of their own.

Caring for babies in hospitals

Some health authorities employ trained early years workers to care for babies on maternity units and in Special Care Baby Units, but the opportunities are decreasing as the care of sick babies becomes more technically demanding.

Babysitting

When parents trust you to baby-sit, they are placing their child's safety in your hands. Babysitting is one of the biggest responsibilities you will ever accept. It is wise to take some precautions when accepting a new babysitting job:

▶ Know your employer: only accept jobs from people you already know or for whom you have reliable, personal references.

▶ Make sure that your parent (or someone you live with) knows where **you** are babysitting. Leave them the name, address and telephone number of the people you are sitting for, and let them know what time to expect you home.

▶ Find out what time the parents expect to be home. Let them know if you have a curfew. Ask them to call if they are running late.

▶ Compile a checklist and make sure you fill it in before the parents leave:

Babysitter's checklist

1) Address of the house ....
2) Phone number at the house ....
3) Name and phone no. of GP ....
4) Nearest hospital and number ....
5) Where the parents will be ....
6) Phone number where the parents can be reached ....
7) What time the parents are expected home ....
8) Name and phone number of neighbours ....
9) Other contacts e.g. grandparents ....
10) Any allergies or special medical info. for children ....

NB: This checklist is also useful to keep next to the phone if you are employed as a nanny

Safety tips for nannies and babysitters

Before the parents leave, ask for the information on the checklist above. Keep the list near the phone at all times:

> ▶ If the house has an electronic security system, learn how to use it.
> ▶ Do not open the door to strangers. Don't let anyone at the door or on the phone know that you're there alone. If asked, respond by saying that you're visiting, the children's parents cannot come to the door and that you'll deliver a message.
> ▶ If you plan to take the children out, make sure that you have a key to lock and unlock doors; don't forget window locks.
> ▶ When you get back to the house, don't go inside if anything seems unusual – broken window, door open etc. Go to a neighbour and call the police.
> ▶ Make sure that you have an escort home if babysitting at night.

In an emergency

- If there is a fire, get the children and yourself OUT! Go to a neighbour's and call the fire department – dial 999. If you can, call the parents and let them know where you and the children are, and what is happening.
- Try not to panic during an emergency. It will not only prevent you from thinking clearly, but will frighten the children.
- If you suspect that a child has swallowed a poisonous substance, call 999 immediately. Be able to identify the poison and the amount taken.

The responsibilities of a professional early years worker

The skills required by the professional early years worker need to be practised with regard to certain responsibilities:

1. Respect for the principles of confidentiality

Confidentiality is the preservation of secret (privileged) information concerning children and their families, which is disclosed in the professional relationship. It is a complex issue that has at its core the principle of trust. The giving or receiving of sensitive information should be subject to a careful consideration of the needs of the children and their families; for example, a child who is in need of protection has overriding needs which means that all relevant information must be given to all the appropriate agencies, such as social workers, doctors etc.

Within the child care and education setting, it might be appropriate to discuss sensitive issues, but such information must never be disclosed to anyone *outside* the setting.

2. *Commitment to meeting the needs of children*

The needs and rights of all children should be paramount and the early years worker must seek to meet these needs within the boundaries of the work role. Any personal preferences and prejudices must be put aside; all children should be treated with respect and dignity, irrespective of their ethnic origin, socio-economic group, religion or disability. The equal opportunities code of practice will give detailed guidelines.

3. *Responsibility and accountability in the workplace*

The supervisor, line manager, teacher or parent will have certain expectations about your role and your responsibilities should be detailed in the job contract; as a professional, you need to carry out all your duties willingly and to be answerable to others for your work. It is vital that all workers know the lines of reporting and how to obtain clarification of their own role and responsibility. If you do not feel confident in carrying out a particular task, either because you do not fully understand it, or because you have not been adequately trained, then you have a responsibility to state your concerns and ask for guidance.

4. *Respect for parents and other adults*

The training you have received will have emphasised the richness and variety of child-rearing practices in the UK. It is an important part of your professional role that you respect the wishes and views of parents and other carers, even when you may disagree with them. You should also recognise that parents are usually the people who know their own children best; in all your dealings with parents and other adults, you must show that you respect their cultural values and religious beliefs.

5. *Communicate effectively with team members and other professionals*

The training you have received will have emphasised the importance of effective communication in the workplace. You will also be aware of the need to plan in advance for your work with babies; knowledge of babies' needs in all developmental areas will enable you to fulfil them within your own structured role. As a team member, good practice will depend on liaising with others, reporting and reviewing your practice. Conflicts between team members often arise from poor communication: for example, a child care worker who fails to report, verbally or in writing, that a parent would be late that day in collecting his baby may cause conflict when a colleague challenges his conduct.

Stress and conflict in the workplace

There are various reasons why conflicts arise in the workplace. The nature of the caring relationship imposes particular stresses that can lead to conflict between team members. Stress and conflict can also occur in the family setting. There may be:

- **low morale** – if individuals feel unsupported and undervalued in their role;
- **confusions over individual roles** in the hierarchy of the organisation; in the family home there may be confusion over specific duties;
- **the responsibility and accountability** of providing care for babies who are ill or disadvantaged;
- **lack of communication** with managers, colleagues and employers;
- **ambiguity** over which tasks should take priority during the working day;
- **excessive workload** – (quantitative i.e. having too much work to do, and qualitative i.e. finding work too difficult);
- **feelings of personal inadequacy and insecurity** often following destructive criticism of one's work.

Contributing to team meetings

Team meetings are usually held regularly and are conducted according to an agreed agenda. Ideally, the written agenda should be given to all team members and include a space for anyone to add their own item for discussion. Certain factors may detract from the value of team meetings:

- **distractions** – constant interruptions, either from telephone calls or visitors;
- **irrelevant topics** – some meetings become a forum for gossip or other topic irrelevant to the task in hand;
- **dominating member** – one person may be aggressive and outspoken, with the effect of blocking other people's contributions.

Assertiveness makes communication at team meetings more effective – it should not be confused with loudness or aggressive behaviour. Assertiveness may be defined in this context as standing up for your basic rights and beliefs, without isolating those of others, and making your behaviour 'match' your feelings. You are expressive with your feelings, without being unpleasant.

Staff appraisal

People need to have feedback on their performance and to know that they are doing well. Appraisal of staff is a means of working with staff to identify their strengths within their work role. It should be viewed by staff as a positive action – even when there are criticisms of performance – which helps to promote good practice within the work setting; most appraisals are carried out annually and by interview. Appraisals are also useful in identifying staff development needs for the individual; for example, an early years worker who is lacking in assertiveness may be sent on an assertiveness training course.

GRIEVANCE AND COMPLAINTS PROCEDURES

If a dispute arises in the workplace, either among employees or between employers and employees, it must be settled; this is usually achieved at an early stage through discussion between colleagues or between the aggrieved person and his immediate superior. If, however, the grievance is not easily settled, then an official procedure is needed.

Caring for babies with special needs

The term special needs is now used to describe children whose development differs from the normal. The aim is to see the individual child first and *then* the special need or disability. The basic needs of the baby – for stability, security and protection – should come before the special needs occasioned by the disability. Babies with special needs will need:

- food
- shelter, warmth, clothing
- cleanliness
- love and security
- praise and recognition
- appropriate specialist care and therapy
- fresh air and sunlight
- sleep, rest and activity
- protection from infection and injury
- new experiences
- responsibility
  day care facilities with key worker
- support

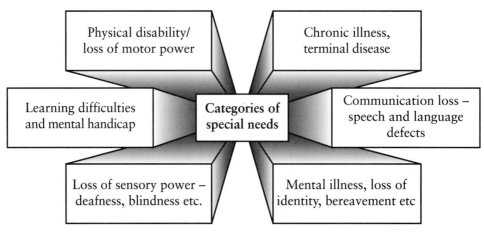

Figure 9.4   Categories of special needs

Sometimes the special need is identified before birth or soon after birth; other special needs may become apparent much later, for example a heart disorder or a visual or hearing impairment.

Babies with special needs may be grouped into the following categories:

- **physical impairment**: problems with mobility or co-ordination. *Examples:* cerebral palsy, spina bifida, sickle cell disease, cleft lip or palate.
- **sensory impairment**: visual or hearing impairment
- **learning difficulties**: problems with cognitive or intellectual function. *Examples:* Down's syndrome, Fragile X syndrome, brain injury from e.g. meningitis.
- **emotional difficulties**: emotional and behaviour difficulties will not usually be evident until later on in childhood; however the root causes may be traced back to deprivation in the first years of life.

NB: It should also be noted that a child may have a *temporary* special need e.g. when a baby's parent or sibling has died or when she is suffering from an acute illness.

Effects on the family

Every parent expecting a baby hopes that the baby will be perfect, and if the baby is disabled in any way, this will have a social, psychological and financial effect on the family and the way it functions. Each family is unique in the way that it will react initially and adjust in the long term. When a mother gives birth to a baby who has a disability, she may experience feelings of guilt – 'It must be because of something I did wrong during pregnancy' – or even of rejection, albeit temporary. Although each family is unique, there are certain common reactions to the birth of a baby with special needs; these include:

> ▶ **A sense of tragedy** – parents who give birth to a child with a disability experience complex emotions; they may grieve for the loss of a 'normal' child but to offer loss counselling in the same way as for a bereavement negates the fact that the child is a child first and foremost and there is no other child to grieve for. Relatives and friends are embarrassed by their own reactions and their awkward response can leave the parents feeling very isolated at a time which is normally spent in celebrating.
> ▶ **Feelings of guilt** and shifting the blame onto someone or something else; this may occur when the special need is caused by an inherited disorder or if the mother ignored health advice during the pregnancy.
> ▶ **Fear of making mistakes** – sometimes there is an over-reliance on professional help; the disability is seen first and parents believe that only a medical expert can advise on the care of their baby, whereas the reality is that the parent will almost always know what is required.
> ▶ **Bonding difficulties**: there may be problems with the bonding process, particularly if the mother and baby are separated for any length of time – or if the mother has fears for the baby's survival;
> ▶ **Stress and anxiety**: tiredness and distress caused by the extra demands involved in the day-to-day care of their baby may result in excessive strain on family relationships; there may also be financial worries brought about by the extra caring responsibilities.
> ▶ **Feeling isolated**: family and friends often have little understanding of a baby that is 'different' in any way; this can result in the parents feeling cut off from normal social relationships.
> ▶ **Resentment**: siblings may resent the disabled baby child who is seen as spoilt or taking up too much of the parents' time.

Supporting the needs of the family

The family needs support – practical and emotional – both during the initial period of grief and adjustment, and during the routine daily care of their baby. Some ways in which early years workers and other professionals could help are by:

✓ **supporting the parents**: understanding and listening to any concerns, simply 'being there' for them;

✓ **having empathy**: try to imagine yourself in the parent's situation – think how you would like to be helped?

✓ **being patient**: always be patient when working with babies, particularly where communication may be difficult or time-consuming;

✓ **offering practical help**: by arranging help on a regular basis, or by referring the parents to the social services department or to a local special needs support group;

✓ **being aware**: an open-minded and non-judgmental attitude is important as is a warm, friendly manner;

✓ **encourage positive images** of babies and children with special needs by using appropriate posters and books in nursery settings;

✓ **being positive** – praise effort rather than achievement and provide activities that are appropriate for the baby's ability so that they have a chance of achieving the goal.

Services for babies with special needs

1. Statutory services

The National Health Service

During her first year a baby may be informally assessed to determine her needs and how those needs may best be provided for. Care available within the health service includes:

- **advice and support from health visitors**; some authorities also employ Special Needs Health Visitors;
- **hospital specialist care**: e.g. paediatricians, orthopaedic surgeons, neurologists, ophthalmologists and other specialist consultants;
- **Primary Health Care Team**: general practitioners (GPs), community paediatric nurses, health visitors and community midwives deal with daily health care, immunisations, and loan of medical equipment for use in the home.

The Social Services Department

All Social Services Departments are required by the Children Act 1989 to set up and maintain a confidential register of children with disabilities. Services include:

- **specialist social worker**: offers professional support, advice and counselling

- **day care provision**: day nurseries, family centres, child-minding facilities, toy libraries;
- **family aide provision**: practical assistance in the family home;
- **respite care**: provision of care on a temporary basis, to allow the family of the baby to have a holiday;
- **financial advice and help**: cash grants, equipment loans and help with transport costs (e.g. to and from nursery) may be available.

Child development centres

In some areas, teams of professionals (doctors, therapists, health visitors, social workers), usually working from what is known as a child development centre, are available to help support children with special needs and their families.

2. Voluntary services

There are many national and local groups concerned with offering support to those caring for babies with special needs. Such support includes:

- **respite care**: some charities and other voluntary organisations offer a form of respite care where a child is taken out for a few hours by a trained volunteer;
- **advice**: many organisations offer practical advice relevant to the particular need;
- **self-help groups**: these groups offer support for carers, who may meet to share problems and for social activities;
- **pressure groups**: these groups work towards influencing policy-makers and planners of services and increasing awareness of the problems faced by informal carers;
- **training for carers**: some organisations offer training courses in specific techniques to improve the delivery of care: for example, the Portage home learning programme.

The Portage home learning programme

The Portage programme was first developed in Wisconsin, USA, in 1970, as a **peripatetic** learning programme for children with moderate developmental difficulties, in order to overcome the problem of the large geographical distance between families. It has since spread rapidly across the UK and in other countries. It is now the most widespread parental participation programme in the UK and is almost exclusively used by families with children of nursery school age.

Figure 9.5   Playing and learning

The Portage programme works on the assumption that parents are willing and capable of participating actively in remediation and teaching. A typical programme is:

1 The home teacher visits the family on a regular basis (usually weekly or fortnightly) at home and sets up a structured teaching programme.
2 The home teacher and the parent jointly assess the child's current level of developmental achievements with the Portage checklist. This checklist underpins the developmental curriculum of the programme and focuses on what the child **can do**.
3 The checklist is used as a basis for deciding on a set of teaching goals.
4 The home teacher shows how a longer-term goal can be broken down into smaller achievable steps.
5 The home teacher then sets up a play/teaching activity to help the child attain a particular step and shows the parent how to carry out the activity through modelling and verbal feedback.
6 The parent tries out the activity in the presence of the home teacher, and is shown how to fill in a standard recording form.
7 In between visits, the parent continues the teaching programme on a daily basis with their child.
8 At the next visit, the home teacher reviews the child's progress with the parent, and then decides whether the child is ready to progress to the next stage of the programme.

There have been criticisms of the programme from educationalists. These criticisms centre on the programme's lack of a theoretical rationale for the items included on the checklist, and on the underlying assumption that the child with special needs develops in a similar sequence to the normally developing child. However, the programme is very popular with most parents and is seen by many as an important means of fulfilling their child's potential. Portage home teachers often act as the family's **key worker** (as envisaged by the DES Warnock Report, 1978) and provide enormous support and assistance.

Contracts and legislation relating to caring for babies

Conditions of employment
The Employment Protection Act (1978) and The Employment Acts (1980 and 1982) require that any employee who works for more than sixteen

hours a week should have a **contract of employment**. The essential features of any employment contract should include:

- Your name and the name of your employers.
- The title of your job and the starting date.
- The scale of pay; the amount of your salary (gross or net), and
  - how it is to be paid, e.g. directly into your bank account or by cheque;
  - when it is to be paid – e.g. weekly or monthly;
  - tax and National Insurance arrangements. Your employer should provide you with a monthly statement showing what deductions have been made.
- Hours of work, detailing starting and finishing times each day, and noting any special arrangements for overtime or extra babysitting.
- Sick pay arrangements.
- Holiday entitlement and holiday pay, including days off at weekends and Bank Holidays.
- Pension payments: for nannies, these are usually arranged by the individual employee, but this should be stated in the contract.
- Duties: the scope of your duties should be detailed – e.g. for nannies – cooking for the children, doing their laundry and cleaning their rooms.
- Length of probationary period; most employers include a four-week probationary period in order to assess your suitability.
- Period of notice: the usual period of notice on either side is one week during the first month and four weeks afterwards.
- Sackable offences: any offences which may lead to your dismissal or any disciplinary procedures should be noted.

Some nanny contracts detail what you may expect in terms of accommodation, meals and the use of the family phone etc. Those applying for jobs within the private sector may want to consider using a reputable nanny agency; such agencies are used to negotiating contracts that suit both employer and employee.

Codes and policies in the workplace

A code of practice is not a legal document, but it gives direction and cohesion to the organisation for which it has been designed. Codes of practice and policy documents cover areas of ethical concern and good practice, such as:

- equal opportunities
- confidentiality
- staff/children ratios
- child protection

A specimen contract for a nanny

Specimen Nanny Contract of Employment

Date of issue: . . . .
This is a contract between (Employer's names) and (your name). (Your name) is contracted to work as a nanny by (Employer's name) at (Employer's address), starting on (Starting Date).

General information

The employers are solely responsible for accounting for the employer's and employees National Insurance and Income Tax contributions. Employers should ensure that they have employer's public liability insurance to cover them should the nanny be injured in the course of work.

Remuneration

The salary is . . . . per *week/month *before/after deduction of Income Tax and national Insurance payable on . . . . The employers will ensure that the employee is given a payslip on the day of payment, detailing gross payment, National Insurance and Income Tax deductions and net payment. Overtime will be paid at £ . . . . net per hour or part thereof. The salary will be reviewed *once/twice a year/on the date of . . . .

Hours of work

The employee will be required to work (hours) . . . . (days of the week) . . . . and may be called upon for baby-sitting up to (nights per week) . . . . In addition, the employee may be required to work overtime provided that . . . . days' notice have been given and agreed in advance. Overtime will be paid in accordance with the overtime detailed in the paragraph

above. In addition, the employee will be entitled to . . . . *days/weeks paid holiday per year. In the first or final year of service, the employee will be entitled to holidays on a pro rata basis. Holidays may only be carried into next year with the express permission of the employers. Paid compensation is not normally given for holidays not actually taken. The employee will be free on all Bank Holidays or will receive a day off in lieu by agreement.

Duties (please specify)

. . . .

The employee shall be entitled to:

a) Accommodation ☐
b) Bathroom *sole use/shared ☐
c) Meals (please specify) ☐
d) Use of car *on duty/off duty ☐
e) Other benefits:

Sickness

The employer will pay Statutory Sick Pay (SSP) in accordance with current legislation. Any additional sick pay will be at the employer's discretion.

Termination

In the first four weeks of employment, one week's notice is required on either side. After four weeks continuous service, either the employer or the employee may terminate the contract by giving . . . . weeks notice.

Confidentiality

The employee shall keep all affairs and concerns of the employers, their household and business confidential, unless otherwise required by law.

Discipline

Reasons which might give rise to the need for disciplinary action include the following:

a) Causing a disruptive influence in the household.
b) Job incompetence.
c) Unsatisfactory standard of dress or appearance.
d) Conduct during or outside working hours prejudicial to the interest or reputation of the employers.
e) Unreliability in time keeping or attendance.
f) Failure to comply with instructions and procedures.
g) Breach of confidentiality clause.

In the event of the need for disciplinary action, the procedure will be firstly, an oral warning; secondly, a written warning, and thirdly, dismissal. Reasons which might give rise to summary dismissal include drunkenness, theft, illegal drug-taking, child abuse.

Signed by the employer . . . .

Date . . . .

Signed by the employee . . . .

Date . . . .

*delete as necessary

- safety aspects
- first aid responsibilities
- partnerships with parents
- record-keeping
- staff training
- food service

Equal Opportunities Policy

An Equal Opportunities Policy represents a commitment by an organisation to ensure that its policies do not lead to any individual receiving less favourable treatment on grounds of:

- sex
- race
- ethnic or national origins
- marital status
- disability
- religious belief
- skin colour

It does *not* mean reverse discrimination in favour of black people. An effective policy will establish a fairer system in relation to:

- recruitment
- training, and
- promotion opportunities.

Policy statement

Each employing organisation should set out a clear policy statement that can be made available to employees and service users. The statement should include:

- recognition of past discrimination;
- a commitment to redress inequalities;
- a commitment to positive action.

Training should be provided to explain to all staff the implications of the policy and its practical consequences. The organisation must also provide information about the law on direct and indirect discrimination. Any policy that attempts to promote equality is only effective if the individuals working in the organisation incorporate its principles into their individual practice. Some suggestions for implementation are:

- Always inform about and encourage ethnic minority staff to apply for training programmes and promotion.
- Encourage all staff to accept that racial and ethnic variations should not be ignored but rather recognised positively in the context of care.
- All staff should be aware that attitudes or actions based on racial prejudice are unprofessional and unacceptable in the workplace.
- Take up the interests of ethnic minority staff and find out whether

there are special needs for canteen, social or cultural facilities; for
religious holidays etc.
• Try to ensure better participation of ethnic minority staff in team
  meetings, case conferences. For example, include on the agenda
  'multiracial and multicultural aspects of care'.

Health and safety policies

Every employer has a duty to protect employees at work and to keep them
informed about health and safety. In general, the employer's duties include:

✓ making the workplace safe and without risks to health;
✓ keeping dust, fumes and noise under control;
✓ ensuring plant and machinery are safe and that safe systems of work are set
  and followed;
✓ ensuring that articles and substances are moved, stored and used safely;
✓ providing adequate welfare facilities;
✓ supplying information, training and supervision necessary for the health
  and safety of employees.

In addition, the employer must:

• draw up a health and safety policy statement if there are more than 5
  employees and bring it to the attention of employees;
• provide free, any protective clothing or equipment specifically required
  by health and safety law;
• report certain injuries, diseases and dangerous occurrences to the
  enforcing authority;
• provide adequate first aid facilities;
• consult a safety representative about issues which affect health and
  safety in the workplace;
• set up a safety committee if asked in writing by two or more safety
  representatives.

There are other more specific duties e.g. concerning overcrowding and
hygiene; these vary from one workplace to another.

The employee has legal duties too, which include:

• taking reasonable care for his or her own health and safety and that of
  others who may be affected by what is done or not done;
• co-operating with the employer on health and safety;
• not interfering with, or misusing, anything provided for the employee's
  health, safety or welfare.

Trade unions and professional organisations

Trade unions and professional organisations exist to represent and protect members' interests. Their main functions are to:

> ▶ negotiate for better pay and conditions of service;
> ▶ provide legal protection and support;
> ▶ represent members at grievance and disciplinary hearings.

Two organisations which early years workers can join are:

* UNISON – a union for health workers
* Professional Association of Nursery Nurses (PANN)

In addition to representing their members' interests, most trade unions and professional organisations publish newsletters and hold regular local meetings to discuss workplace issues.

Professional development of the early years worker

Working in the field of child care and education can be physically and emotionally exhausting, and professionals will need to consolidate their skills and be reflective in first employment. It is important to keep abreast of all the changes in child care practices by reading relevant journals, such as *Nursery World*, *Infant Education* etc., and by being willing to attend in-service courses when available.

Activities relating to Chapter 9

ACTIVITY I

Qualities in caring

Think about the qualities outlined above on page 190.

* Do you feel you already possess these qualities?
* Do you think academic knowledge is important for someone working in care organisations?

Evaluate your own interpersonal skills:

Can you empathise – i.e. put yourself in someone else's situation. Think of someone you know who has a problem and focus on viewing the world as that person sees it. Write a description of a 'day in the life' of the person you have chosen, told from their viewpoint.

ACTIVITY 2

A welcoming start

In your work placement, find out the following information:

1 How welcoming is the setting? Describe the factors which help to create a welcoming environment and list any possible improvements.
2 How safe is the setting? Try to look at the setting from a child's viewpoint and again list any possible improvements.

ACTIVITY 3

Settling in at a day nursery

Plan a routine for settling in a baby over her first few weeks at a day nursery. Try to implement the routine and evaluate it.

ACTIVITY 4

Special needs

Research the condition Down's Syndrome, including the following points:

- the cause;
- the incidence in the UK and world-wide;
- the characteristics of a child with Down's Syndrome;
- the prognosis and help available.

ACTIVITY 5

Job search

Write a specimen advertisement stating what sort of job you would like; try to give a prospective employer a good idea of your personality and your abilities and be realistic in your demands.

Appendix:
Emergency Procedures

If a baby appears unconscious and gives no response, use this ABC of resuscitation

A Airway – open the airway

> ▶ Place the baby on a firm surface
> ▶ Remove any obstruction from the mouth
> ▶ Put one hand on the forehead and one finger under the chin, and gently tilt the head backwards **very slightly**. (If you tilt the head too far back, it will close the airway again.)
>
>

B Breathing – check for breathing

> ▶ Put your ear close to the baby's mouth
> ▶ Look to see if the chest is rising or falling
> ▶ Listen and feel for the baby's breath on your cheek
> ▶ Do this for five seconds

If the baby is *not* breathing:

1 Start **MOUTH TO MOUTH-AND-NOSE RESUSCITATION.**

> ▶ Seal your lips around the baby's mouth and nose.
> ▶ Blow gently into the lungs until the chest rises.
> ▶ Remove your mouth and allow the chest to fall.

2 Repeat five times at the rate of one breath every three seconds.
3 Check the pulse.

C Circulation – check the pulse

Lightly press your fingers towards the bone on the inside of the upper arm and hold them there for five seconds.

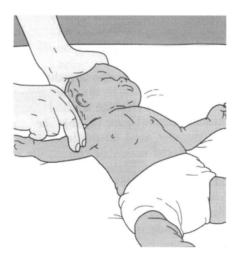

If there is *no* pulse, or the pulse is slower than 60 per minute, and the baby is *not* breathing, start chest compressions:

1 Find a position one finger's width below the line joining the baby's nipples, in the centre of the breastbone.
2 Place the tip of two fingers on this point and press to a depth of about 2 cm ($\frac{3}{4}$ inch) at a rate of 100 times per minute.

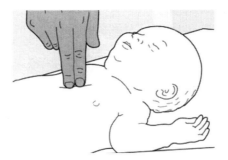

3 After five compressions, blow gently into the lungs once.
4 Continue the cycle for one minute.
5 Carry the baby to a phone and **dial 999 for an ambulance**.
6 Continue resuscitation, checking the pulse every minute until help arrives.

If the baby is *not* breathing but *does* have a pulse:

1 Start MOUTH TO MOUTH-AND-NOSE RESUSCITATION at the rate of one breath every three seconds.

2 Continue for one minute, then carry the baby to a phone and **dial 999 for an ambulance**.

If the baby *does* have a pulse and is breathing:

1 Lay the baby on her side, supported by a cushion, pillow, rolled–up blanket or something similar.
2 Dial 999 for an ambulance.
3 Check breathing and pulse every minute and be prepared to carry out resuscitation.

Choking

Check inside the baby's mouth. If the obstruction is visible, try to hook it out with your finger, but don't risk pushing it further down. If this doesn't work, proceed as follows:

> ▶ Lay the baby face down along your forearm with your hand supporting her head and neck, and her head lower than her bottom. OR:
> ▶ An older baby or toddler may be placed face down across your knee with head and arms hanging down.
> ▶ Give five brisk slaps between the shoulder blades.
> ▶ Turn the baby over, check the mouth and remove any obstruction.

> ► Check for breathing.
> ► If the baby is not breathing, give five breaths (see **MOUTH TO MOUTH-AND-NOSE RESUSCITATION** page 217).
> ► If the airway is still obstructed, give five **CHEST COMPRESSIONS**.
> ► If the baby is still not breathing, repeat the cycle of back slaps, mouth to mouth-and-nose breathing and chest compressions.
> ► After two cycles, if the baby is not breathing, dial 999 for an ambulance.

NB: Never hold a baby or young child upside down by the ankles and slap their back – you could break their neck.

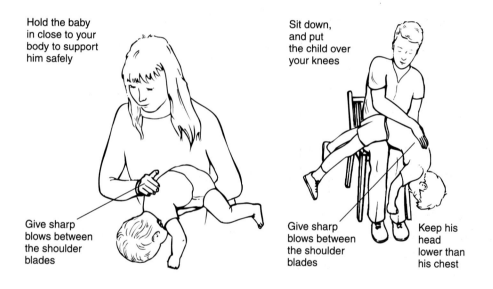

Hold the baby in close to your body to support him safely

Give sharp blows between the shoulder blades

Sit down, and put the child over your knees

Give sharp blows between the shoulder blades

Keep his head lower than his chest

Head injuries

Babies and young children are particularly prone to injury from falls. Any injury to the head must be investigated carefully. A head injury can damage the scalp, skull or brain.

Symptoms and signs

If the head injury is mild, the only symptom may be a slight headache and this will probably result in a crying baby. More seriously, the baby may:

> ▶ lose consciousness even if only for a few minutes;
> ▶ vomit;
> ▶ seem exceptionally drowsy;
> ▶ complain of an ache or pain in the head;
> ▶ lose blood from her nose, mouth or ears;
> ▶ lose any watery fluid from her nose or ears;
> ▶ have an injury to the scalp which might suggest a fracture to the skull bones.

Treatment

If the baby or young child has any of the above symptoms:

Dial 999 for an ambulance or go straight to your nearest A & E department

Meanwhile:

> ▶ if the child is unconscious, follow the ABC routine described on page 216–217;
> ▶ stop any bleeding by applying direct pressure, but take care that you are not pressing a broken bone into the delicate tissue underneath; if in doubt, apply pressure around the edge of the wound, using dressings;
> ▶ if there is discharge from the ear, position the child so that the affected ear is lower and cover with a clean pad; do not plug the ear.

Glossary

Accommodation
The process by which children modify their existing schemas in order to incorporate or adapt to new experiences (Piaget).

Adaptation
Fitting in with – and thriving in – the environment. In Piaget's theory, adaptation is achieved through the complementary processes of assimilation and accommodation.

Allergen
A substance capable of producing allergy or particular hypersensitivity.

Allergy
Hypersensitivity acquired through exposure to a particular allergen.

Amenorrhoea
The absence of menstrual periods.

Anaemia
A condition in which the concentration of the oxygen-carrying pigment, haemoglobin, in the blood is below normal.

Anterior fontanelle
A diamond-shaped soft area at the front of the head, just above the brow. It is covered by a tough membrane; you can often see the baby's pulse beating there under the skin. The fontanelle closes between 12 and 18 months of age.

Areola
The pigmented ring around the nipple.

Assimilation
The process by which children incorporate new experiences into their existing schema (Piaget).

Attachment
An enduring emotional bond that infants form with specific people, usually starting with their

mothers, sometime between the ages of 6 and 9 months.

Attention deficit disorder

A disorder of childhood characterised by marked failure of attention, impulsiveness and increased motor activity.

Bilirubin

Everyone's blood contains haemoglobin found in red blood cells. Red blood cells live only a short time and, as they die, the oxygen-carrying substance (haemoglobin) is changed to yellow bilirubin. Normal newborns have more bilirubin because their liver is not efficient at removing it.

Blastocyst

Hollow fluid filled ball of cells formed after fertilisation.

Blood transfusion

The infusion of large volumes of blood or blood components directly into the bloodstream.

Bonding

A term used to describe the feelings that parents have for their children.

Breech presentation

During labour the baby is lying with bottom or feet downwards.

Cervical smear test

A test to detect abnormal changes in the cervix (the neck of the womb) and so prevent the development of cervical cancer.

Chromosome

A thread-like structure in the cell nucleus that carries genetic information in the form of genes.

Colostrum

A creamy yellowish fluid produced by the breasts during pregnancy. Low in fat and sugar, it is uniquely designed to feed the newborn baby.

Counselling

A process of guidance and advice offered by a trained counsellor to someone who is experiencing difficulties.

Cytomegalovirus   One of the family of herpes viruses. A pregnant woman can transmit the virus to her unborn child; this may cause malformations and brain damage in the child.

Diabetes mellitus   A disorder caused by insufficient production of the hormone insulin by the pancreas.

Ectopic pregnancy   A pregnancy that develops outside the uterus, most usually in the fallopian tube.

Eczema   An inflamed red rash common in babies and children.

Embryo   The unborn child during the first eight weeks of development following conception.

Fallopian tube   The tube that extends from the uterus to the ovary.

Fever (or pyrexia)   A temperature above 37°C (37°C is the normal body temperature).

Foetal alcohol syndrome   A pattern of physical and mental abnormalities due to maternal alcohol intake during pregnancy.

Foetus   The unborn child from the end of the eighth week after conception until birth.

Folic acid   A vitamin of the B complex. It is involved in the synthesis of amino acids and DNA. Green vegetables, liver and yeast are major sources of folic acid in the diet.

Fundus   The top of the uterus.

Gestation   The length of time, or duration, of a pregnancy.

Gluten   The protein present in rye, wheat, barley and oats.

Haemolytic disease of the newborn   A disease in which there is excessive destruction of the red blood cells in the foetus and the neonate, resulting in jaundice. It is usually caused by Rhesus incompatibility between the infant's blood and the mother's.

Hypertension   Abnormally high blood pressure (the pressure of blood in the main arteries).

Hypoglycaemia   An abnormally low level of sugar (glucose) in the blood.

Incubator   A warmed perspex box for nursing pre-term and ill babies.

IVI (intravenous infusion)   The therapeutic introduction of a fluid, such as saline, into a vein.

Jaundice   Yellowness of the skin due to excessive bilirubin in the blood.

Membranes   Tough membranes which surround the amniotic fluid in which the baby floats in the womb.

Neonate   A newly born infant under the age of one month.

Oedema   An abnormal accumulation of fluid in the body tissues. In pregnancy, oedema is often shown as swollen ankles and fingers.

Phototherapy   Treatment of disease by exposure to light, as in jaundice in the newborn.

Placenta   The organ that develops in the uterus during pregnancy and links the blood supplies of mother and baby – often referred to as the 'afterbirth'.

Plaque   A rough, sticky coating on the teeth that consists of saliva, bacteria and food debris.

Pre-eclampsia   A serious condition in which hypertension, oedema and protein in the urine develop in the latter part of the pregnancy.

Projectile vomiting   Vomiting with the material projected with great force.

Schema   A mental framework or structure which encompasses memories, ideas, concepts and programmes for action which are pertinent to a particular topic.

Self concept   The individual's view, acquired through life experiences, of all the perceptions, feelings, values and attitudes that define 'I' or 'me'.

Socialisation   The process by which children learn the culture or way of life of the society into which they are born.

STD (Sexually Transmitted Disease)   Infection transmitted primarily, but not exclusively, by sexual intercourse.

Stool   The faecal discharge from the bowels.

Swaddling   A method of wrapping the newborn baby securely in a blanket.

Therapy   Any treatment of disease.

Tracking   Also called smooth pursuit. The smooth movements of the eye use to follow the track of some moving object.

Uterus   Another name for the womb.

Vaginal pessary   A medicated vaginal suppository.

Varicose veins   Enlarged or twisted superficial veins, usually in the legs (varicose veins of the anus are called haemorrhoids or piles).

Ventilator   An apparatus that is designed to qualify the air that is breathed through it.

Bibliography and References

Bruce, T. and Meggitt, C. (1996) *Child Care and Education*. London: Hodder & Stoughton.

Coffey, J. (1998) *Health Care for Children*. London: Hodder & Stoughton.

Einon, D. (1985) *Creative Play*. Harmondsworth: Penguin Books.

Flanagan, C. (1996) *Applying Psychology to Child Development*. London: Hodder & Stoughton.

Hilton, T. (1991) *The Great Ormond Street Book of Baby and Child Care*. London: The Bodley Head.

Johnston, P.G.B. (1994) *The Newborn Child*. Edinburgh: Churchill Livingstone.

Karmiloff-Smith, A. (1994) *Baby It's You*. London: Embury Press.

Leach, P. (1997) *Your Baby and Child*. Harmondsworth: Penguin Books.

Meadows, S. (1992) *Understanding Child Development*. London: Routledge.

Meggitt, C. (1997) *Special Needs for Health and Social Care*. London: Hodder & Stoughton.

St John's Ambulance (1992) *First Aid Manual*. London: Dorling Kindersley.

Thomson, H. and Meggitt, C. (1997) *Human Growth and Development*. London: Hodder & Stoughton

Whiting, M. and Lobstein, T. (1992) *The Nursery Food Book*. London: Edward Arnold.

Index